EXERCITATIO ANATOMICA
DE MOTU CORDIS ET SANGUINIS
IN ANIMALIBUS

Oil portrait of William Harvey in 1628 when he was fifty years of age. In that year his *de Motu Cordis* was published. This picture was acquired by the Royal College of Physicians in 1909, but the artist is unknown. Note the "anatomical table" of the arterial circulation, similar to the preparation by Harvey still in the possession of the Royal College of Physicians.

—Courtesy of the Oxford University Press.

(Fifth Edition, Second Printing)

EXERCITATIO ANATOMICA
DE MOTU CORDIS
ET SANGUINIS IN ANIMALIBUS

BY WILLIAM HARVEY, M.D.

An English Translation
with Annotations by

CHAUNCEY D. LEAKE

CHARLES C THOMAS · PUBLISHER

SPRINGFIELD, ILLINOIS, U.S.A.

M.CM.LXX

This Modern English Translation
is reproduced
from the 1928 Tercentennial Edition

of

EXERCITATIO ANATOMICA
DE MOTU CORDIS
ET SANGUINIS IN ANIMALIBUS

By WILLIAM HARVEY, M.D.

as presented by
CHAUNCEY D. LEAKE

The Tercentennial Edition, 1928. In cloth.
Presenting a *facsimile* of the original Latin edition and an English
Translation.
Second Edition, 1931. In paper.
Presenting an English Translation.
Third Edition, 1941. In paper.
Presenting an English Translation.
Third Edition, Second Printing, 1949. In paper.
Fourth Edition, 1958. In paper.
Fifth Edition, 1970. In paper.
Fifth Edition, Second Printing, 1978. In paper.

ISBN 0-398-00793-4

Library of Congress Catalog Number: 74-143744

Printed in the United States of America

00-2

CONTENTS

LIST OF ILLUSTRATIONS

WILLIAM HARVEY (1578-1657)

From the painting in the Royal College of Physicians of London by C. Janssen (1590-1664)
who lived in England from 1618 to 1648.

—Courtesy of the Oxford University Press.

PREFACE

NOTE TO THE FOURTH EDITION

Exceptional interest was shown in Harvey and his work on the tercentennial of his death in 1657. A special occasion was held at the Royal College of Physicians in London, on June 3, the day he died. This included a considerable symposium, with a new color edition of the famed "Harvey Film," which Sir Henry Dale so fittingly introduced. Professor Kenneth J. Franklin offered a new English translation of *De Motu Cordis* (Blackwell, Oxford, & C. C. Thomas, Springfield, Ill., 220 pp.). Louis Chauvois, the distinguished French medical historian, gave an excellent interpretive biography (Hutchinson, London, 304 pp.). Many significant addresses were made: The Harveian Lecture by Sir Arthur Salusburg MacNalty at the Health Congress of the Royal Society of Health at Folkestone, Harvey's birthplace, on "William Harvey: His influence on Public Health" (*Roc. Soc. Health Journ.*, 77: 324–337, 1957); Doctor Carl J. Wiggers' Harvey Society Lecture, "The Impact of Harvey and his Work on Circulation Research (*Circul. Res.*, 5: 335–348, 1957); Professor V, Kruta's "Harvey in Bohemia (*Physiol. Bohemoslo.*, 6: 433–438, 1957), and Doctor K. F. Russell's "Homage to Harvey" (*Med. Journ. Australia*, 1: 777–781, June 8, 1957). Special exhibits, with symposia discussions, were held by the New York Medical College (where Professors Felix Marti-Ibanez and Douglas Guthrie spoke), by the Los Angeles Heart Association, and by the National Heart Institute and the National Library of Medicine, where the speakers included Doctors James Watt, James Shannon, Frank Rogers, Charles O'Malley, Frederick Kilgour, Andre Cournand, Theodore Hilbish and Walter Lillehei. Interestingly, the USSR issued a large brown forty kopek commemorative stamp, showing the Royal College of Physicians portrait (in reverse).

[ix]

PREFACE

The Los Angeles and Washington discussions focused attention on the detailed extension of knowledge about the heart and circulation since Harvey's time, and the extraordinary applications of this knowledge to transfusion, to the management of cardiovascular disease, and to the success of cardiovascular surgery. They also indicated how much of Harvey's path-finding effort remains unfinished. Importantly, they reminded people everywhere of the significance of the basic scientific methodology which Harvey introduced. It was a time for stock-taking in human and mammalian cardiovascular physiology and its applications, and much was made of it. Surprisingly, however, there was little comment on Harvey's work on generation.

In the nearly two decades since the last edition of this annotated translation, many new contributions have been made to our knowledge of Harvey and to the fundamental and applied extensions of his great demonstration. All of these deserve comment and review: indeed, a comprehensive bibliography of three centuries of Harveian literature is long overdue. Harvey's meticulous student, Geoffrey Keynes, has revised his *"Bibliography of the Writings of Dr. William Harvey"* (Cambridge University Press, 1953), and devoted a Linacre Lecture to "The Personality of William Harvey" (Cambridge University Press, 1949, 47 pp.), with an account of the portrait of Harvey which was rescued from his brother's home at Rolls Park, Essex. At this time, however, only a few comments are justified on some of the more significant recent developments of our knowledge of Harvey's cardiac studies and their subsequent expansion.

Interesting recent discussions have appeared on various aspects of the history of our knowledge of the heart and circulation. Outstanding has been the appreciation of the work of Ibn Nafis (1210–1288), who first described the pulmonary circulation. While this work was apparently unknown to Harvey, he would probably have made little use of it anyway; as Professor Donald Fleming insists so well, "The pulmonary circulation was not central for his purpose." The most thorough account of Ibn

Nafis with a translation and full bibliography was given in the William Osler Medal Essay by Dr. E. A. Bittar (*Bull. Hist. Med.*, 29: 352–368; 429–447, 1955).

Professor Fleming has analyzed Galen's work on the motion of the blood in heart and lungs (*Isis*, 46: 14–21, 1955) and has also carefully considered William Harvey's discussion of the pulmonary circulation (*Isis*, 46: 319–327, 1955). Professor Fleming indicates that Harvey was really not the successor of Colombo on the pulmonary circulation, nor willingly a precursor of Thomas Bartholin (1616–1680) on the lymphatic system. Harvey went directly to the central problem of the systemic circulation in animals.

Five recent developments are of interest in regard to Harvey's report on the circulation; the possible influence of Leonardo da Vinci (1452–1519) on Harvey; ballistocardiagraphic analysis of Harvey's observations on the force of the heart beat; current interest in venous return to the heart; the significance of blood distribution in regulating circulation, and the increasing clinical applications of cardiovascular physiology.

First, the question may be raised as to whether or not Harvey knew of the amazing Leonardine drawings on the heart valves and on eddy flow in the blood vessels. These have been well reproduced and annotated by K. O. Keele (*Leonardo da Vinci* on the *Movement of the Heart and Blood*, Harvey and Blythe, London, 1952, 160 pp.). They had been kept by the descendants of Leonardo's heir, Melzi, not far from Padua, and may have been seen occasionally by distinguished visitors. Andreas Vesalius (1514–1564), the great Paduan anatomist, may have been one, as well as his follower Girolamo Fabrizzi (1533–1619), Harvey's teacher. That Harvey knew of them might have been a factor in their acquisition by Lord Arundel, with whom Harvey travelled, when the Leonardine drawings were being dispersed.

Second, the recent ingenious method of recording the impact of blood thrust in a human by ballistocardiography resulted in skilled analysis of the force of the heart beat as commented upon by Harvey. Doctor Isaac Starr of the University of Pennsylvania is a notable contributor to this advance (*J. Clin. Invest.*, 25: 53, 1945). This procedure may also give some indication of cardiac output and its variations in disease. Cardiac catheterization methods, developed by Cournand and Richards (*J. Clin. Invest.*, 24: 106, 1945) also give valuable information on cardiac output in health and disease. The applications of these methods to cardiac surgery have been spectacular.

Third, the problem of venous return to the heart, as outlined by Harvey, has recently received increased interest. This has raised again the question as to whether or not the ventricles of the heart exert any suction action in affecting venous return. These matters have been carefully studied by Professor Gerhard Brecher (*Venous Return*, Grune & Stratton, New York, 1956, 158 pp.).

Fourth, the recognition of blood reservoirs by Joseph Barcroft (1872–1947) has resulted in growing appreciation of the significance of blood distribution in regulating circulation. This matter has been reviewed by Professor T. Sjostrand (*Physiol. Rev.*, 33: 202–268, 1953). This concept has been skillfully extended by Professor Howard Swann to local reservoirs of blood for pressure maintenance in connection with filtration functions as in the kidneys, the eyes, and certain glands (*Science*, 115: 64, 1952; *Am. J. Ophthal.*, 38: 845, 1954; *Texas Rep. Biol. Med.*, 13: 251, 1955).

Finally, it is pertinent to remind ourselves that Harvey's brilliant demonstration of blood circulation in mammals had to wait a couple of centuries for successful clinical application in humans. The obvious application in blood transfusion, widely attempted within a few decades of Harvey's death, failed tragically for reasons not clear until Karl Landsteiner (1868–1943) demonstrated antigenic factors in human bloods in 1900, thus opening the way for successful blood typing and effective clinical use of transfusion and blood substitutes.

PREFACE

During the rapid use of scientific (i.e. quantitative) physiology in the 19th Century, quick clinical applications of Harvey's work became possible. As he forsaw, blood circulation became important in understanding the pathological progress of infectious disease. As various blood pressure correlations were made with cardiovascular pathology, significant new means were found for accurate diagnosis, and subsequent efforts at treatment. This story has been well told by Professor Arthur Ruskin (*Classics in Arterial Hypertension*, C. C. Thomas, Springfield, Ill., 1956, 358 pp.).

It is now 30 years since this effort in interpreting Harvey's work for the benefit of curious moderns first appeared. Gratifying to me has been the continued interest in Harvey's work on the heart and circulation. It was particularly pleasing in 1957 to realize worldwide interest in Harvey's endeavor, appropriately debated in connection with the tercentenary of his death. It is both humbling and exalting to appreciate what has been accomplished since Harvey's time in understanding the way in which the heart and circulation functions in animals and how this information may be helpfully applied to the promotion of human health. Popular concern over the matter is well illustrated in the extensive public support of such an agency as the American Heart Association. Through the devoted efforts of thousands of intelligent lay people, significant funds are collected annually and used in large part for the advance of knowledge on the heart and circulation, as first outlined by William Harvey three centuries ago. The accelerating pace of effective application of this knowledge to human health gives promise that cardiac disease, which has become so important with the increasing life span, may be more satisfactorily controlled and prevented. But then what? Can we also make our lives more worth the living?

C. D. L.

The Ohio State University, Columbus,

PREFACE TO FIRST EDITION

Veritas nos liberabit

As far as I can find, this is the fourth attempt to render Harvey's classic into current English idiom. The first was apparently an anonymous effort prefaced by a Zachariah Wood of Rotterdam, and printed by Francis Leach for Richard Lowndes of London, in 1653. This octavo was reprinted in 1673, and again in beautiful format by the Nonesuch Press in 1928, under the editorial direction of Mr. Geoffrey Keynes. The second by Michael Ryan, appeared in Volumes I and II of the London Medical and Surgical Journal, 1832–33. The third was the well known translation made for the Sydenham Society by Robert Willis and published in 1847. Reprinted in London in 1889, in Canterbury in 1894, and in Everyman's Library in 1907, this has become the standard English version. Although an excellent translation, its stilted and involved phraseology makes it rather difficult reading for those more accustomed to modern diction. As Mencken has intimated in connection with similar classics, this greatly interferes with their proper appreciation. From my rather limited experience with medical students and physicians, I am confident that they would welcome the chance to study the works of the great contributors to their profession were these to be offered to them in an attractive and easily readable form.

This prompted Mr. Thomas to suggest, when we discussed a tercentennial edition of Harvey's great book, that a new translation in the language and spirit of our times be attempted. Using Willis as a guide, this has been an easy and delightful task. In his more scientific passages, Harvey is remarkably terse and "snappy," in the current style. In his philosophical discussions he becomes vague and his sentences grow beyond control, but whose do not?

PREFACE

Not possessing a copy of the first edition, the basis of my translation was the miserably printed Longhine edition of 1697, which omits the dedication. Willis's translation of the dedication has been included here: from it one may get some idea of the Cavalierian grace of his style. After my friend, Dr. John Fulton, kindly sent me a copy of Moreton's privately printed facsimile of the original edition, I found several errors in the text I had used. This fortunately necessitated careful collation, resulting in some corrections in the English version.

The translation is admittedly free, in the deliberate attempt to present Harvey's thought in the current physiological manner. Thus, while Harvey nowhere actually uses a word which may be literally rendered "pump," it is our habit to refer to cardiac action in some such term.

The differences in Harvey's style through the book imply its composition at different times. The introduction is far more vigorous, and in its critical attitude, more characteristically youthful than any of the remaining seventeen chapters. The first chapter, on the other hand, apologizing for the effort, has the grace and dignity of careful deliberation, and closes with a classical quotation reflecting the meditative calm of middle age. The last three chapters add little to the significance of the demonstration. They illustrate the futility of theoretical speculation attempting to reconcile opposing points of view with inadequate data. With microscopical technique undeveloped, Harvey could not see the communications between arteries and veins. He tried later to study the problem by a sort of corrosion method, but failed to find anything resembling an anastomosis except in three obscure places. At the time, he tried to complete his demonstrations by metaphysical arguments based on the traditional teleology. This was the antithesis of the method by which he had achieved such brilliant success in the preceding chapters.

The last of the book seems to have been written some time after the main part of it, when long reflection on the subject had crystallized his opinion. The eighth chapter is similar in style and context to the fifteenth and sixteenth, and was, I think, written at about the same time.

The argument in the other chapters from two to fourteen proceeds with certain characteristics that introduced an entirely new method of approach in physiological problems. These are (1) the careful analysis of phenomena observed (chapters two to five); (2) the devising of experimental procedures to test a proposed hypothesis (chapters ten, eleven, and thirteen), and (3) the startling innovation of quantitative reasoning to prove a proposed theory (chapters nine, ten, and thirteen). Harvey was among the first to use the practical methods of science as we do now: observation, hypothesis, deduction, and experiment. This is neither scholastic Aristotelianism nor Bacon's laborious accumulation of data and its manipulation by the cumbersome tables of the *Novum Organum*. The sixth and seventh chapters, on the pulmonary circulation, are puzzling. There is a good discussion of the comparative and embryological aspects of the subject, and then a peculiar use of the traditional authority of Galen as evidence. One may find almost all kinds of logic in Harvey.

In order to bring out the significance of Harvey's work in regard to our modern knowledge of cardiac function, and to relate it to the slow development of this knowledge, footnotes have been added to the translation. I hope they will appeal to medical students and interested laymen. For specialists in the history of medicine, they may seem superfluous, in spite of my effort to make them as brief and inconspicuous as possible. Most of the information in them has been culled from the standard authorities in physiology and its history. A running account of the development of Harvey's demonstration and its influence was to have been appended, but will have to wait till later. A chronology of his life has been added. For my information and point of view I am indebted to a host of Harvey enthusiasts, Haeser, Willis, Munk, Foster, Dalton,

PREFACE

Curtis, Osler, D'Arcy Power, Hemmeter, Garrison, and Singer. For scholarly inspiration I am grateful to Dr. George Sarton, Dr. Percy Dawson, and Dr. William Snow Miller. For cheerful support in this and similar fancies I owe much to my wife's interest, and to that of the genial members of the Dick Marshall Dining Club. I am especially thankful to the Oxford University Press for kind permission to reproduce several of the splendid illustrations from *Portraits of Dr. William Harvey* (1913).

Many efforts were made in 1928 to celebrate appropriately the tercentennial of the appearance of Harvey's great book. The Royal Society of Physicians of London and the Harvey Society of New York held special festivals. R. Lier and Co. of Florence issued a facsimile of the original work. The Nonesuch Press reprinted the first English translation, and Mr. Geoffrey Keynes published an authoritative bibliography of Harvey's writings. While these challenge the attention of connoisseurs, this volume has been prepared chiefly in the hope that it may interest medical and advanced zoological students, by offering in a dignified but inexpensive way an opportunity to become acquainted, intellectually, with one of the greatest contributors to their subjects. To that end the publisher and printers have done more than their share to make my little part easy.

It has been a delight to work with Mr. Thomas in the preparation of this volume, and I appreciate his continued courtesy and enthusiasm.

C. D. L.

Madison, Wisconsin, 1928

NOTE TO THE SECOND EDITION

Thanks to the kind interest of Dr. John F. Fulton, Sterling Professor of Physiology at Yale University, this second edition was made possible and especially prepared by the publisher for medical students at an exceptionally low price. Dr. Fulton generously provided me with material for notes on the "Thebesian Vessels", and otherwise suggested valuable improvements. A number of additions and corrections have been made, chiefly to the notes, in the attempt to correlate Harvey's work as closely as possible with present physiological conceptions of the circulation of the blood.

It was hoped originally to append a brief running account of the historical development of ideas regarding the circulation. This has been rendered superfluous by the appearance of many interesting essays on Harvey and his work, which were issued in connection with the Tercentenary Celebration of the publication of his *De Motu Cordis*. Among these should be mentioned Doctor Archibald Malloch's book (New York, Paul Hoeber, Inc., 1929) and papers by Doctors Alfred E. Cohn (Ann. Med. Hist., n.s. 1, 16, 1929), E. B. Krumbhaar (*ibid.*, p. 57), J. J. R. MacLeod (*ibid.*, 10, 338, 1928), F. R. Packard (*ibid.*, p. 498), and Sir Humphrey Rolleston (*ibid.*, p. 323).

Experience with medical students has justified the conviction that one of the best ways by which to gain an introduction to the physiological knowledge of the heart and circulation is through the study of Harvey's brief and brilliant classic. It is a significant exercise in general culture as well. The foot-notes have been planned to support the interest of such a reading by provocative reference to present physiological research bearing on Harvey's work and to such historical factors as may contribute to a better appreciation of his intellectual courage and achievement.

Once more it is a pleasure to acknowledge the kind efficiency and generous cooperation of Mr. Thomas in making this publication possible. I am also most grateful indeed to Dr. Fulton not only for this cordial interest in this venture, but particularly for his friendly understanding in connection with certain phases of it.

C. D. L.

San Francisco, 1930

NOTE TO THE THIRD EDITION

In spite of the acute impact of political and economic events, the less tangible cultural relations between different countries may be more significant in the long run. For these shape the direction of political and economic forces. With today's threat to the achievement of our cultural ideal, every opportunity should be taken to strengthen the desire to maintain it. Harvey's great classic stands solidly and large in the foundation of modern science. Not dictated by any economic or political consideration, it challenges recent sweeping claims of dialectic materialists regarding the evolution of science. It follows the ancient altruistic tradition of science. This has been maintained most effectively in recent times by application of the English gentleman's concept of *noblesse oblige*. Clear and clean this stands against the cloudy tendency to conceal scientific information for commercial or political purposes. Ever since Platonic times has science had an implicit relation to ethics, in respect to motives or purposes, but only recently has this relation become significant in a broad social way. The spirit and aim of science, in the humble sense of ascertaining as best we can what is the relative "truth" about ourselves and our environment, has rarely been exemplified more succinctly than by Harvey. This spirit may have powerful aesthetic and moral significance when one considers how the knowledge so obtained may be applied.

If this edition of Harvey's masterpiece shall help inspire anyone with his spirit, it will have served its purpose. My sincere thanks as always to Charles C Thomas for his encouraging insistence that another edition should appear.

Since the last edition a number of interesting reviews relating to recent work on the heart and circulation have been published: J. Barcroft, "Fetal Circulation and Respiration," *Physiol. Rev.*,

16: 103, 1936; E. W. H. Cruickshank, "Cardiac Metabolism," *Physiol. Rev.*, 16: 597, 1936; T. R. Harrison, "Arterial and Venous Pressure Factors and Circulatory Failure," *Physiol. Rev.*, 18: 86, 1938; J. H. Burn, "Sympathetic Vasodilator Fibers," *Physiol. Rev.*, 18: 137, 1938; E. R. Clark, "Arterio-Venous Anastomoses," *Physiol. Rev.*, 18: 229, 1938; A. Blalock, "Experimental Hypertension," *Physiol. Rev.*, 20: 159, 1940; H. C. Bazett, "Peripheral Circulation," *Ann. Rev. Physiol.*, 1: 163, 1939; J. A. E. Eyster, "Heart," *Ann. Rev. Physiol.*, 1: 317, 1939; E. M. Landis, "The Peripheral Circulation," *Ann. Rev. Physiol.*, 2: 125, 1940; L. N. Katz, "Heart," *Ann. Rev. Physiol.*, 2: 181, 1940; A. Grollman, *The Cardiac Output of Man in Health and Disease*, Springfield, Ill., C. C Thomas, 1932, xiv+325 pp.; E. P. Boas, *The Heart Rate*, Springfield, Ill., C. C Thomas, 1932, xi+160 pp.; K. J. Franklin, *A Monograph on Veins*, Springfield, Ill., C. C Thomas, 1937, xxii+410 pp.; G. B. Anrep, *Studies in Cardio-Vascular Regulation*, Stanford University, 1936, 118 pp.; A. J. Clark, *Comparative Physiology of the Heart*, N. Y., Macmillan, 1927, 157 pp.; *Ergebnisse der Kreislaufforschung*, Berlin, 1+, 1931+; E. K. Marshall, Jr., "The Cardiac Output of Man," *Medicine*, 9: 175, 1930; T. R. Harrison, *Failure of the Circulation*, Baltimore, Williams & Wilkins, 1935, xii+396 pp.; and numerous articles by various authorities in *Heart, Ergebnisse für Physiologie, Biologische Chemie, und Experimentellen Pharmakologie*, and other review journals. Current scientific activity in the field is well illustrated in the symposium edited by F. R. Moulton, *Blood, Heart and Circulation*, Publication of the American Association of the History of Science, No. 13, Washington, D. C., 1940, 331 pp., by 53 contributors.

This list is restricted to articles dealing with the basic physiology of the heart and circulation. This keeps the bibliography in reasonable relation to Harvey's work. On this basis I excluded reference to extensive works dealing with therapeutics of cardiovascular disease, digitalis, electro-cardiography, cardio-vascular roentgenology, and cardio-vascular pathology. To the list of

PREFACE

recent works relating to Harvey should be added the important biographical study by Sir Wilmot Herringham, "The Life and Times of Dr. William Harvey," *Ann. Med. Hist.*, N. S., 4: 109–125; 249–272; 347–363; 491–502; 575–589, 1932; the survey of Harvey's literary background by D. F. Fraser-Harris (*Proc. Roy. Soc. Med.*, 27: 1095–1099, 1934); H. Wade's account of Harvey in Scotland (*Edin. Med. J.*, 45: 761–781, 1938); G. H. Evans' Harveian pilgrimage (*Calif. West. Med.*, 48: 447–449, 1938); certain recent Harveian orations (R. Hutchison, *Brit. Med. J.*, 2: 733–739, Oct. 21, 1931; W. L. Brown, *Lancet*, 2: 961–967, Oct. 24, 1936; H. Yellowlees, *Edin. Med. J.*, 44: 695–706, 1937); and the observations of Ludwig Aschoff, *Über die Entdeckung des Blutkreislaufs*, Freiburg i. B., H. Speyer, 1938.

Meanwhile the first edition of Harvey's classic in Spanish translation appeared (*Harvey: Iniciador del Metodo Experimental*, Mexico, 1936, xvii+398 pp.) with the brilliant introduction and annotations by the distinguished Mexican physiologist, Dr. J. J. Izquierdo. As part of the observance of the tercentenary of the publication of Harvey's masterpiece, V. Meisen prepared its first Danish translation and published it in appropriate format with an historical introduction and epilogue: *William Harvey's Bog om Opdagelsen af Blodets Kredsløb*, 1929, xxviii+103 pp. Professor John F. Fulton, whose interest in this effort has been a continued inspiration to me, writes that Professor Nicolai I. Propper has mentioned a Russian translation appearing in 1937. Well-known are the German translations of R. Ritter von Topley, *William Harvey, Die Bewegung des Herzens und des Blutes.* (*Klassiker der Medizin herausgegeben von Karl Sudhoff*), Bd. 1, Leipzig, J. A. Barth, 1910, 120 pp.; and J. H. Baas, *William Harvey, der Entdecker des Blutkreislaufs*, Stuttgart, F. Enke, 1878, 116 pp.; and the French version of Charles Richet, *William Harvey, La Circulation du Sang*, Paris, G. Masson 1879, 287 pp. Meisen refers to a partial Swedish translation by Robert Tigerstedt which appeared in Stockholm in 1921. Gradually then direct scientific influence and appreciation of the great English biologist is spreading in modern cultures. Perhaps it may sometime help in cementing them closer together in the growing realization of the basic biological principle that survival of groups of living things depends on mutual adaptation to each other. With humans this carries the implication that the adaptation must be to mutual satisfaction, and thus condemns any form of power politics.

C. D. L.

San Francisco, 1941

PREFACE

TO THE FIFTH EDITION

THE preparation of the Fifth Edition of this little effort in connection with Harvey's classic poses a problem. Should I attempt a complete revision of the notes? This would be expensive. Part of my purpose has been to make Harvey's great classic readily available to students in the health professions at a relatively low price. Charles C Thomas of Springfield, Illinois, helped very greatly with the First Edition, reproducing in facsimile the 1628 Frankfurt classic. It was a worthy production. He then went on of offer it in paperback for the purpose of making it readily and inexpensively available to students in the health professions. I think I should continue this tradition with respect to this item. If I were to revise the notes, it would mean resetting the entire book, and this would be expensive. Besides, if I let the notes stand as they are, it will save me a lot of trouble. Further, the notes as they are, giving a reasonably fair indication of what the state of cardiovascular knowledge was in 1628, have historical interest.

On the other hand, I can take the opportunity in this introductory note to the Fifth Edition to call attention to some of the many recent contributions which have been made to our knowledge and understanding of Harvey's work. As might be expected, our English colleagues have been particularly productive and stimulating in this regard. Their efforts have always been characterized by the most meticulous scholarship and one can say now that we have almost a definitive understanding of William Harvey and his great practical and philosophical contribution.

Noteworthy were the outpourings of praise in connection with

Harvey during the tercentennial of his death. Many of these I noted previously. Some deserve further comment. For the tercentennial of Harvey's death, the late Doctor Kenneth J. Franklin (1901–1964) published a new translation of Harvey's classic, *The Movement of the Heart and Blood in Animals* (Blackwell Scientific Publications, Oxford, 1957). This was distinguished by the first reproduction of the Rolls Park 1622 portrait of William Harvey through the courtesy of Doctor Myron Prinzmetal of Los Angeles. Doctor Franklin also issued translations of Harvey's correspondence (*The Circulation of the Blood*, Oxford, 1958), from which Sir Geoffrey Keynes quoted extensively.

Outstanding is the *Life of William Harvey* by Geoffrey Keynes, Kt. (Oxford, 1966, 501 pp.). This may be considered the definitive biography of William Harvey. It was preceded by a more popular biographical account, *William Harvey the Man, the Physician, and Scientist*, by Kenneth D. Keele (Nelson, London, 1965). Doctor Keele's volume was one of the series of "British Men of Science." Sir Geoffrey Keynes' biography is detailed, and meticulously documented. He succeeds thoroughly in separating fact from opinion, and yet he gives the full and rich impression of a complex and vigorous character. This volume is well illustrated, and beautifully printed.

It is interesting that there should have appeared almost simultaneously two excellent English translations of Harvey's manuscript *Lectures on the Whole of Anatomy*. The first was by Professors C. D. O'Malley, F. M. L. Poynter and K. F. Russell. This annotated translation of *Prelectiones Anatomiae Universalis* (University of California Press, Berkeley, 1961, 239 pp.), was taken from the Sloane manuscript in the British Museum, a facsimile edition of which was published in 1886. This neat volume has as its frontispiece the Rolls Park family portrait of William Harvey, made around 1622. This picture is being well preserved by Doctor Myron Prinzmetal of Los Angeles, who is generous in permitting its reproduction. The O'Malley translation is quite literal, and the notes are voluminous and helpful. It translates through the 98th recto page of the manuscript. The deciphering of Harvey's almost illegible handwriting must have been a tough job. It was appropriate that it should have been carried through so well by the late Professor O'Malley (1907–1969) with the pleasant surroundings of the great rare book collection of the University of California at Los Angeles, in association with his close friend, Doctor Poynter, the distinguished director of the Wellcome Historical Medical Library in London, and with Professor Russell of Melbourne. This was truly an intercontinental achievement.

A couple of years later, Doctor Gweneth Whitteridge edited, translated, and annotated *The Anatomical Lectures of William Harvey: Prelectiones Anatomiae Universalis: De Musculis* (The Royal College of Physicians, London, 1964, 568 pp.). This important effort, giving a Latin transcription of Harvey's difficult manuscript through the 98th recto, goes on to the following 68 pages of the manuscript which describe the muscles of the humerus and scapula and the muscles of other parts of the body, with a concluding note on the distinguishing features of muscles. This section on muscles is the first publication of this interesting and significant work of William Harvey. This volume has a scholarly introduction and the free translation has been well edited for readability so as to avoid the disjointed aspects of Harvey's notes. Doctor Whitteridge published a note on the growth of Harvey's ideas on the circulation of the blood at about the same time (*Brit. Med. J.*, 2: 7–12, July 2, 1966). She also edited and translated Harvey's notes for a treatise, *De motu locali animalium* (Cambridge, 1959). This was among the Sloane manuscripts in the British Museum. Her transcription of these rough notes makes them intelligible. These notes comprise the "observations on the organic motion of animals and the structure of muscles" referred to in Note 10 to Chapter XVII of my translation of *De Motu Cordis*.

Another interesting Harvey item was by the distinguished

PREFACE

medical historian, Walter Pagel, *William Harvey's Biological Ideas: Selected Aspects and Historical Background* (S. Karger, Basel, 1967). These various recent books on Harvey were reviewed by L. S. King (*J. Amer. Med. Assoc.*, *200:* 961–963, June 12, 1967). The front cover of this issue of *JAMA* again carries the 1622 portrait of William Harvey through the courtesy of Doctor Myron Prinzmetal.

Walter Pagel's ever interesting studies on Harvey's philosophical attitudes continue apace. His discussion of the purpose of the circulation as outlined by Harvey (*Isis*, *42:* 22–38, 1951) was followed by a consideration of the influence of the baroque obsession with circles as exemplified by the circular scholastic argument of A. Cesalpino (1524–1604) about the movement of blood and the quantitative demonstration by Harvey (*J. Hist. Med.*, *12:* 140–157, 1957). With Pyarali Rattansi, Pagel described Harvey's 1636 visit in Prague with Marcus Marci (1595–1667) while on the Arundel mission (*Med. Hist.*, *8:* 78–84, 1964). Marci and Harvey exchanged information on the circulation and on generation, and Harvey's demonstration gained another European supporter. With M. Winder, Pagel explored Harvey's expression of the implications of blood circulation in relation to blood as a vector of infection and as a distributor of chemicals, even when they are applied to the skin (*Bull. Hist. Med.*, *42:* 496–509, 1968).

In his remarkable Institute for Medical History in Rome, Professor A. Pazzini arranged an exceptional exhibit of Harviana (*Guglielmo Harvey nel Tricentenaria della Morte*, Soc. Ed. Universo, Rome, 1957, 92 pp.). In a keen study of Harvey's influence on the philosophy of science, J. A. Passmore showed (*Australasian J. Philos.*, *36:* 85–94, 1958) that Harvey demolished the *a priori* assumption that it is impossible to describe organic or living processes in mechanical terms. Perhaps this was what attracted R. Descartes (1596–1650) to Harvey's demonstration, in spite of Harvey's avowed Aristotelean vitalism. In

[xxvii]

developing G. Bassalla's note on Harvey's analogy of the heart
as a pump (*Bull. Hist. Med.*, *36:* 467–470, 1962), C. Webster
shows that the specific notion of the heart as a pump came to
Harvey after the 1628 publication of *De Motu Cordis* (*Bull. Hist.
Med.*, *39:* 508–517, 1965). The reference to a water-bellows in the
1616 *Prelectiones* is claimed to be a later interpolation. The clear
pump analogy appears in the second letter (1649) to Riolan. The
idea may have been suggested to Harvey by Walter Warner
(1550–1640) in connection with fire-engine bellows pumps which
were coming into use in England around 1630. Previous to this
Harvey had stressed the muscular action of the heart, with an
innate vital force, a position criticized by Descartes. As I pointed
out in Note Six to Chapter XVII *De Motu Cordis*, Harvey did
not use any specific Latin word which properly or literally could
be translated "pump." Nevertheless I was bold enough to give
the "pumping" rendition, since this was clearly Harvey's meaning, even though he expressed it in the conventional technical
terminology of the Galenical and Aristotelean tradition. He
used the technical physiological language of his day, and this
changed slowly as new concepts came along, including the idea of
the heart as a pump.

Other recent commentaries on Harvey's brilliance include: a
short but important note on Cesalpino and Harvey by that keen
physiology scholar, J. J. Izquierdo (*Riv. Stor. Med.*, *5:* 124–128,
1961); a careful discussion by W. L. Von Brunn of Harvey's
Aristoteleanism, which led him to hold to the vitalistic idea that
heat generates motion, ignoring the Paduan physicists except in
respect to quantitation (*Kreislauffunktion in William Harvey's
Schriften*, Springer, 1 Berlin 1967, 171 pp.); Erna Leskey's previous discussion of the Aristotelean influences in Harvey's
embryology in regard to his concept of circularity with heat
generating motion (*Arch. Gesch. Med.*, *41:* 370–380, 1957); R. J.
Durling's discovery (*Med. Hist.*, *8:* 279–281, 1964) of a short
verse in praise of Harvey in a 1624 attack on quacks by Peter

Bowne (1575-1624); E. and S. Hey's account of the law-suit between William Smith and Harvey, in which Harvey's shrewd caution is revealed both in treating patients and in money matters (*J. Hist. Med.*, *24:* 3-21, 1969); the posthumous appearance of Charles Donald O'Malley's pleasant account of the lure of Padua for training great English physicians, such as Thomas Linacre, John Caius, and William Harvey, who received their doctorates in medicine in 1496, 1541, and 1602 respectively (*Med. Hist.*, *14:* 1-9, 1970); and the article by H. Buess showing Harvey's influence in respect to quantitation on Daniel Bernoulli (1700-1782), Leonard Euler (1707-1788) and Albrecht Von Haller (1708-1777), with the later giving experimental support to Harvey's ideas in the first of his nine volume *Elementa Physiologia* (Lausanne, 1757), using injections and microscopic tracings to lay a foundation for modern hemodynamics (*Med. Hist.*, *14:* 175-182, 1970).

Thanks to Professor John Sevringhaus, we had a pleasant opportunity, recently, to hear interesting family tradition about Harvey from Professor F. J. W. Roughton of Cambridge. He is an eighth generation nephew of Harvey, descended from the latter's brother, Daniel, whose son was the English Ambassador to Turkey. This seminar on July 10, 1968, at the University of California in San Francisco, led all who participated to feel truly empathic toward that austere seventeenth century biomedical scientist, William Harvey.

Thus, pleasant browsing continues among the many writings on the life, times, and achievements of William Harvey. In every instance respect grows for his skill, his intellectual ability, his care and caution, and his amazing vigor. My hope, in preparing this preface to the fifth edition of my annotated translation of his classic *De Motu Cordis*, now over 40 years old, is that some of the flood of young growing biomedical scientists, and budding members of the health professions and services, may be inspired by the significance of Harvey's achievement, and thus stimulated to probe deeply, even as he did, into the mysteries of life.

Our times are perilous and troublesome, even as were Harvey's. Maybe it would be helpful for us to follow his example in doing our daily jobs as well as we can, and in carrying our burdens with equanimity. "Activism" seems to be the watch-word for our young intellectuals, along with "relevance," and "y'know." The former is about as meaningless as the latter. One of our thoughtful students, Harry Ackley, recently put it well (*Science, 168:* 1526, June 26, 1970), "A republic cannot long survive without respect for its institutions or adherence to agreed upon processes of dissent." Harvey gave an excellent example of the successful use of an agreed upon process of dissent. He knew, when he published *De Motu Cordis*, that he risked his career, his reputation and possibly his life. He had every reason to believe that he was correct in his opinion on the circulation of the blood. He dissented from authority in a dignified and carefully considered manner. He lived to see the acceptance of his new idea. He dissented without disrupting. Maybe our current dissenters could benefit by following Harvey's example.

Few publishing houses can equal the amazing record set by Charles C Thomas in respect to books, monographs and journals in medicine, science, technology and public administration. This has been due to the keen leadership of Payne E. L. Thomas, the dedicated son of Charles C Thomas. My grateful thanks are extended to him in connection with the preparation of this fifth edition of my English translation of Harvey's *De Motu Cordis*, as it has been extended in the past to his father.

C. D. L.

The Upper Haight-Ashbury, San Francisco, 1970

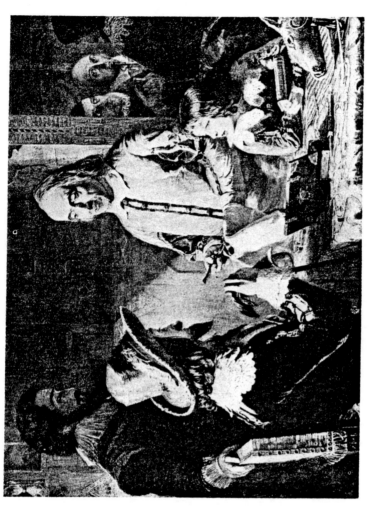

HARVEY DEMONSTRATING TO CHARLES I HIS THEORY OF THE CIRCULATION OF THE BLOOD
Painted by R. Hannah, engraved by H. Leman, published March 25, 1851, by Lloyd Bros. & Co, London
—From a copy in the State of Wisconsin General Hospital

THE FIRST NOTATION OF THE DISCOVERY OF THE CIRCULATION OF THE BLOOD, IN HARVEY'S HANDWRITING

This is the right hand page 80 of Harvey's *Prelectiones Anatomiae Universalis*, his 1616 Lecture Notes, discovered in the British Museum and published in 1886. It reads as follows:

> WH constat per fabricam cordis sanguinem
> per pulmones in Aortam perpetuo
> transferri, as by two clacks of a
> water bellows to rayse water
> constat per ligaturam transitum sanguinis
> ab arterijs ad venas
> vnde Δ perpetuum sanguinis motum
> in circulo fieri pulsu cordis
> An? hoc gratia Nutritionis
> an magis Conservationis sanguinis
> et Membrorum per Infusionem calidam
> vicissimque sanguis Calefaciens
> membra frigifactum a Corde
> Calefit

One may freely translate these rough notes:

WH demonstrates by the structure of the heart that blood is continually passed through the lungs into the aorta, as by two clacks of a water bellows to raise water. The passage of blood from arteries to veins is shown by means of a ligature. So it is proved that a continual movement of the blood in a circle is caused by the beat of the heart. Is this for the sake of nourishing or the better preservation of the blood and parts of the body by infusion of heat, the blood alternately being cooled, by heating these parts, and warmed, by the heart?

EXERCITATIO,
ANATOMICA DE
MOTV CORDIS ET SAN-
GVINIS IN ANIMALI-
BVS,

GVILIELMI HARVEI ANGLI,
Medici Regii, & Professoris Anatomiæ in Col-
legio Medicorum Londinensi.

FRANCOFVRTI,
Sumptibus GVILIELMI FITZERI.
ANNO M. DC. XXVIII.

To The Moſt Illuſtrious and Indomitable Prince CHARLES, KING of GREAT BRITAIN, FRANCE and IRELAND, DEFENDER of the FAITH

MOST ILLUSTRIOUS PRINCE!

The heart of animals is the foundation of their life, the sovereign of everything within them, the sun of their microcosm, that upon which all growth depends, from which all power proceeds. The King, in like manner, is the foundation of his kingdom, the sun of the world around him, the heart of the republic, the fountain whence all power, all grace doth flow. What I have here written of the motions of the heart I am the more emboldened to present to your Majesty, according to the custom of the present age, because almost all things human are done after human examples, and many things in a King are after the pattern of the heart. The knowledge of his heart, therefore, will not be useless to a Prince, as embracing a kind of Divine example of his functions,—and it has still been usual with men to compare small things with great. Here, at all events, best of Princes, placed as you are on the pinnacle of human affairs, you may at once contemplate the prime mover in the body of man, and the emblem of your own sovereign power. Accept, therefore, with your wonted clemency, I most humbly beseech you, illustrious Prince, this, my new Treatise on the Heart; you, who are yourself the new light of this age, and, indeed, its very heart; a Prince abounding in virtue and in grace, and to whom we gladly refer all the blessings which England enjoys, all the pleasure we have in our lives.

Your Majesty's most devoted servant,
WILLIAM HARVEY

(London . . . . 1628.)

(TRANSLATION BY ROBERT WILLIS, M.D., 1847.)

[3]

To His Very Dear Friend
DOCTOR ARGENT

the excellent
and accomplished PRESIDENT *of* THE ROYAL
COLLEGE *of* PHYSICIANS, *and* to other learned
Physicians, his esteemed Colleagues.

I have already and repeatedly presented you, my learned
friends, with my new views of the motion and function of the
heart, in my anatomical lectures; but having now for nine
years and more confirmed these views by multiplied demonstrations in your presence, illustrated them by arguments, and
freed them from the objections of the most learned and skilful
anatomists, I at length yield to the requests, I might say en-
treaties, of many, and here present them for general consideration in this treatise.

Were not the work indeed presented through you, my learned
friends, I should scarce hope that it could come out scatheless
and complete; for you have in general been the faithful witnesses
of almost all the instances from which I have either collected
the truth or confuted error; you have seen my dissections, and
at my demonstrations of all that I maintain to be objects of
sense, you have been accustomed to stand by and bear me out
with your testimony. And as this book alone declares the blood
to course and revolve by a new route, very different from the
ancient and beaten pathway trodden for so many ages, and
illustrated by such a host of learned and distinguished men, I
was greatly afraid lest I might be charged with presumption did

[4]

I lay my work before the public at home, or send it beyond seas for impression, unless I had first proposed its subject to you, had confirmed its conclusions by ocular demonstrations in your presence, had replied to your doubts and objections, and secured the assent and support of our distinguished President. For I was most intimately persuaded, that if I could make good my proposition before you and our College, illustrious by its numerous body of learned individuals, I had less to fear from others; I even ventured to hope that I should have the comfort of finding all that you had granted me in your sheer love of truth, conceded by others who were philosophers like yourselves. For true philosophers, who are only eager for truth and knowledge, never regard themselves as already so thoroughly informed, but that they welcome further information from whomsoever and from whencesoever it may come; nor are they so narrow-minded as to imagine any of the arts or sciences transmitted to us by the ancients, in such a state of forwardness or completeness, that nothing is left for the ingenuity and industry of others; very many, on the contrary, maintain that all we know is still infinitely less than all that still remains unknown; nor do philosophers pin their faith to others' precepts in such wise that they lose their liberty, and cease to give credence to the conclusions of their proper senses. Neither do they swear such fealty to their mistress Antiquity, that they openly, and in sight of all, deny and desert their friend Truth. But even as they see that the credulous and vain are disposed at the first blush to accept and to believe everything that is proposed to them, so do they observe that the dull and unintellectual are indisposed to see what lies before their eyes, and even to deny the light of the noonday sun. They teach us in our course of philosophy as sedulously to avoid the fables of the poets and the fancies of the vulgar, as the false conclusions of the sceptics. And then the studious, and good, and true, never suffer their minds to be warped by the passions of hatred and envy, which unfit men duly to weigh the arguments that are advanced in behalf of truth, or to appreciate the proposition that is even fairly demonstrated; neither do they think it unworthy of them to change their opinion if truth and undoubted demonstration require them so to do; nor do they esteem it discreditable to desert error, though sanctioned by the highest antiquity; for they know full well that to err, to be deceived, is human; that many things are discovered by accident, and that many may be learned indifferently from any quarter, by an old man from a youth, by a person of understanding from one of inferior capacity.

My dear colleagues, I had no purpose to swell this treatise into a large volume by quoting the names and writings of anatomists, or to make a parade of the strength of my memory, the extent of my reading, and the amount of my pains; because I profess both to learn and to teach anatomy, not from books but from dissections; not from the positions of philosophers but from the fabric of nature; and then because I do not think it right or proper to strive to take from the ancients any honour that is their due, nor yet to dispute with the moderns, and enter into controversy with those who have excelled in anatomy and been my teachers, I would not charge with wilful falsehood any one who was sincerely anxious for truth, nor lay it to any one's door as a crime that he had fallen into error. I avow myself the partisan of truth alone; and I can indeed say that I have used all my endeavours, bestowed all my pains on an attempt to produce something that should be agreeable to the good, profitable to the learned, and useful to letters.

Farewell, most worthy Doctors,
And think kindly of your Anatomist,
WILLIAM HARVEY.

(TRANSLATION BY ROBERT WILLIS, M.D., 1847.)

[6]

Introduction

IN DISCUSSING the movements and functions of the heart and arteries, we should first consider what others have said on these matters, and what the common and traditional viewpoint is. Then by anatomical study, repeated experiment, and careful observation, we may confirm what is correctly stated, but what is false make right.

Nearly all anatomists, physicians, and philosophers up to now have thought with Galen[1] that the pulse has the same function as respiration, differing only in one respect, the former arising from an animal, the latter a vital faculty, but from the standpoint of function or movement behaving alike.

[1] Claudius Galenus (131–201) of Pergamos was the most versatile and articulate of Graeco-Roman physicians. His physiological system was derived from Greek and Alexandrian sources and his own observations and experience. Elaborated into a dogma by scholastic effort, it dominated medicine until it crumbled in the 17th century. A. J. Brock has recently translated and commented on his more significant writings (*Greek Medicine*, Lond. and New York, 1929, and *Galen on the Natural Faculties*, Lond. and New York, 1916). Charles Singer has neatly summarized the Galenical system in his *Evolution of Anatomy*, New York, 1925. For a full biobibliography on Galen or any other classical scientist, one should always consult George Sarton's great *Introduction to the History of Science*, Balt., 1927+.

Thus one finds, as in the recent book on *Respiration* by Hieronymus Fabricius of Aquapendente,[2] that since the pulsation of the heart and arteries is not sufficient for the aeration and cooling of the blood, Nature has placed the lungs around the heart. So it seems that whatever has been said prior to this about the systole and diastole of the heart and arteries has been proposed with special reference to the lungs.

Since the movements and structure of the heart differ from those of the lungs, as those of the arteries from those of the chest, separate functions or purposes are likely. The pulsings and uses of the heart as well as of the arteries are distinct from those of the chest and lungs. If the pulse and respiration have the same purpose, if the arteries in diastole draw air into their cavities (as commonly said) and in systole give off waste vapors by the same pores in flesh and skin, and if also in the time between systole and diastole they contain air,[3] in fact containing at all times either air, spirits, or sooty vapors, what may be answered to Galen? He declared that the arteries by nature contain blood and blood alone, neither air nor spirits, as may

---

[2] See note 1, Chapter XIII, for an account of Fabricius.

[3] The word *fuligines* is translated *waste-vapors*. The idea of this supposed *sooty material* may have developed from the duskier hue of venous blood. The intake and output of air to and from the arteries through pores in flesh and skin goes right back to Empedocles (5th Cent. B.C.). Interesting that this should be involved in the first aspect of current opinion about the heart and blood-vessels to be refuted by Harvey.

easily be determined by experiments and explanations found in his report.

If in diastole the arteries are filled by air drawn
in, the greater the pulse the greater being the amount
drawn in, then when the whole body is immersed
in a bath of oil or water, a previously strong pulse
should either become much weaker or slower, for
the bath surrounding the body will make it difficult
if not impossible for the air to enter the arteries.
Likewise, when all the arteries, the deep as well as
superficial, are distended at the same time and with
equal speed, how is it possible for the air to pene-
trate as easily and quickly through the skin, flesh,
and bulk of the body to the deeper parts as through
the skin alone? How may the arteries of the
fetus draw air into their cavities through the mother's
abdomen and the uterine mass? How may seals,
whales, dolphins, other species of cetaceans, and
all kinds of fish in the depths of the sea draw in and
give off air through the great mass of water by the
pulsing systole and diastole of their arteries? To
say that they absorb air fixed in the water and give
off their waste vapors to the water is pure fiction.[4]

---

[4] Of course this is just what they do. The fundamental facts about
respiration were established by A-L. Lavoisier (Hist. Acad. roy. d.
Sci., Paris, 1784, p. 355) and, for internal respiration, by G. Magnus
(Ann. Phys. u. Chem., 1837, 41: 583). The fundamental laws about
gaseous behavior were being developed about 1660 by Robert Boyle
(1627–1691), but I have not been able to find who first showed the
solubility of air in water. The laws governing these phenomena were
studied by Henry in 1803 and by Dalton in 1807. Humboldt and
Provencal first studied the respiration of fishes (Mem. Soc. phys. chim.
d'Arcueil, Paris, 1807, 2: 359).

If the arteries during systole exhale waste vapors from their cavities through the pores of the flesh and skin, why not at the same time the spirits said to be contained within them, for spirits are much more volatile than sooty wastes. Again, if the arteries receive and pour out air in diastole and systole, as the lungs in respiration, why not the same if cut open as in arteriotomy? In cutting open the trachea it is clear that the air goes in and comes out of the wound in two opposite directions. In cutting open an artery it is equally clear that the blood escapes in one continuous direction and that no air either goes in or comes out.

If the pulsations of the arteries cool and purify the various portions of the body as the lungs do the heart, how, as is commonly said, do the arteries carry from the heart to the separate parts the vital blood stuffed with vital spirits, which keep up the heat of these parts, nourish them in sleep, and restore them in exhaustion? How, if the arteries be tied off, do the parts at once become not only torpid, cold, and pale, but even cease to be nourished, unless it be as Galen says that they have been deprived of that heat which flowed through them from the heart? So it would seem that the arteries carry heat to the parts instead of cooling them.

Now, how may the diastole draw spirits from the heart to warm the parts at the same time from the outside to cool them? Further, although some state that the lungs, arteries, and heart have the same function, they also say that the heart is the factory of the spirits and that the arteries contain and transmit them, denying, contrary to the opinion of Columbus,[5] that the lungs either make or contain spirits. Then they declare with Galen that blood is contained in the arteries, and not spirits, contrary to Erasistratus.

It is clear that these opinions are so contradictory and irreconcilable that all are doubtful. Blood is to be found in arteries, and blood alone, as is plain from the experiment of Galen, from arteriotomy, and from wounds. By cutting open a single artery, as Galen states more than once, all the blood may easily be drained from the whole body in a half hour's time. The experiment of Galen referred to

---

[5] Not Christopher but Matheus Realdus (1516–1559). A vain, unscholarly, and unscrupulous man, pupil of Vesalius, and Professor of Anatomy at Rome. In his *De Re Anatomica* (1559), he correctly described the pulmonary circulation, but failed to realize the significance of what he did. He made a distinct advance over the Galenists, however, in thinking that blood was rendered "spiritous" by air in the lungs instead of in the heart. Foster thinks (Hist. of Physiol., 1901, p. 30) he cribbed the description from the unfortunate religious fanatic, Michael Servetus (1510–1553), who was burned under Calvin at Geneva. The latter's *Restitutio Christianismi* (1553) contains a remarkable passage discussing the pulmonary circulation, but since only 3 copies escaped the flames, it obviously could have little influence. Servetus had studied anatomy in Paris with Vesalius. Galen (131–201 A.D.) showed that arteries contained blood, contrary to the opinion of the earlier Greeks, as exemplified by Erasistratus of Alexandria (3rd Century B.C.) who found the arteries empty in dissections of dead bodies. Harvey discusses all these points later.

I have broken into shorter paragraphs, for greater ease in reading, a couple of very long paragraphs through here in the original.

is this: "If you will place two ligatures around an artery and make a longitudinal incision in the portion of the artery between them, nothing but blood will be found." Thus does he prove the arteries contain blood alone. We may reason similarly. Finding the same blood in veins, tied off in a similar manner, that is found in arteries (as I have frequently noted in dead and living animals), we may likewise conclude that arteries contain the same blood as veins and nothing but the same blood.[6]

Some authors, while trying to explain this difficulty in saying that blood is spiritous in the arteries, tacitly allow that the function of the arteries is to distribute the blood from the heart to the whole body, and that the arteries are filled with blood. Spiritous blood is none the less blood, as no-one denies that the blood, even that which flows in the veins, is filled with spirits. Even if the blood in the arteries is very gorged with spirits, it is still believable that these spirits are as inseparable from the blood as those in the veins. The blood and spirits comprise a single fluid (as whey and cream in milk, or heat in hot water) with which the arteries are

---

[6] Harvey was philosophically interested in the ideas about the origin and "perfection" of blood. Not being able to find "spirits" anywhere, he is apparently trying to show that arteries as well as veins contain the same fundamental fluid, blood,—and that there is no "vital" difference between arterial or venous blood. See next paragraph. The chemical difference between arterial and venous blood was demonstrated in 1668 by John Mayow (1643–1679), but due to Stahl's phlogiston theory, his ideas were neglected until they developed through Lavoisier and Magnus, note 2.

filled, and for the distributing of which from the heart the arteries exist. This is nothing else than blood.

If this blood is drawn from the heart into the arteries by their diastole it follows that the arteries in their distention are filled with blood, and not with air, as previously discussed. If they are said also to be filled from the surrounding atmosphere, how and when do they take in blood from the heart? During systole is impossible: the arteries would have to fill while contracted, or to fill and not become distended. During diastole is improbable: they would then receive for two contrary purposes both blood and air, and heat and cold.

Further, when it is stated that the diastole of the heart and arteries is simultaneous, and the systole likewise, there is another inconsistency. How can two bodies being connected together and being distended at the same time draw anything one from the other? Or being contracted simultaneously receive anything one from the other? Moreover, it seems impossible that one body may thus draw another body to itself in order to become distended, since distention is passive, unless return is made to a natural state, like a sponge previously compressed by external force. It is hard to imagine anything like this in the arteries.

The arteries distend because they are filled like bladders or pouches and they are not filled because they expand like a bellows, as I have easily and clearly shown, and proved, I think, ere this. However, in Galen's book, *Quod sang. cont. in Arter.*,[7] there is an experiment to show the opposite: an artery is exposed and cut longitudinally, and a reed or hollow tube is inserted through the opening, so the wound is closed and the blood not driven out. "As long as it stays thus," he says, "the whole artery will pulsate, but if you tie a thread around the artery firmly pressing its tunics against the tube you will see the artery does not beat as fully beyond the noose." I have neither made this experiment of Galen's, nor do I believe it can be done easily in the living body because of the excessive loss of blood from the artery. I doubt that the tube would close up the wound without a ligature, and that blood would not burst out between the tube and the vessel. Yet Galen seems to prove[8] by this experiment both that the pulsating power passes from the heart through the walls of the arteries, and that the arteries while dilating are filled by this pulsating power since they dilate like a bellows and do not distend because they are filled like a leather bottle.

The contrary, however, is apparent in arteriotomy

---

[7] Harvey refers to the tract entitled *An Sanguis in Arteriis Natura Contineatur*, by the translator M. Rota, in the great Froben edition of Galen published in Basle in 1542 (*Operum Galeni Tomus Primus Classem Primam Continet, Quae Humani Corporis Fabricam*, 197).

[8] A little unfair to Galen (131-201 A.D.). Not only was the experiment not tried, but unwarranted conclusions are unjustly ascribed to him. This simile of the bellows and leather bottle is frequently used by Harvey.

and wounds, the blood leaping from the artery rushes out with force, first farther, then nearer, alternately in spurts, the spurt being always during the distention of the artery, never during its contracture. From this it is obvious that the artery is distended by the impulse of blood, for it is impossible for it *per se* to throw the blood with such force while dilating,—it should rather be drawing air into itself through the wound, according to the common ideas on the functions of the arteries.

We should not let the thickness of the arterial walls mislead us into believing that the pulsating power moves along them from the heart.[9] In some animals the arteries do not differ from the veins, and in the distant parts of the body where the arteries are finely divided, as in the brain and hand, no-one can tell arteries from veins by their walls, for the tunics are the same in both. In an aneurysm arising from an injured or eroded artery, the pulse is just the same as in the other arteries, but it has no arterial tunic. The renowned Riolan supports me in this in his 7th Book.

---

[9] As in a peristaltic wave. The elasticity of blood-vessel walls, depending on their elastic fibers and smooth muscle tunics, is now recognized as a factor in maintaining blood pressure. Harvey demonstrated that the pulsation in the arteries is due to their sudden distention by blood forced out of the heart during its contraction. Andreas Caesalpinus (1519–1603) argued this point in his *Quaestiones Peripateticae* (Lib. V, Quaest. 4) in 1571, but without apparently impressing any of the anatomical or medical investigators of his or the next century.

For information on Riolan (on whom Harvey relies in this argument) see Note 1, Chapter IV.

It is not to be supposed that the function of the pulse is the same as that of respiration because the respiration is made more frequent and powerful, as Galen says, by the same causes as running, bathing or any other heating agent. Not only is experience opposed to this (though Galen strives to get around it), when by immoderate gorging the pulse becomes great and the respiration less, but in children the pulse is rapid when respiration is slow. Likewise in fear, trouble, or worry, in many fevers, of course, the pulse is very fast, the respiration slower than usual.

These and other similar inconveniences beset the traditional opinions about the pulse and the functions of the arteries. Those maintained on the function and beat of the heart are perhaps no less involved in many tangled difficulties. The heart is commonly said to be the source and factory of the vital spirits, from which life is given to the different portions of the body, yet that the right ventricle makes spirits is denied,—it merely gives nourishment to the lungs. So it is said that the right ventricle of the heart is lacking in fishes (indeed in all animals in which there are no lungs), and that the right ventricle exists for the sake of the lungs.

1. The structure of both ventricles is practically the same. There is the same fabric of fibers, braces, valves, vessels, auricles, and both on section are filled with similar dark colored and coagulated blood. Why, then, should we imagine their func-

tions to be so different when the action, movement, and beat of both are the same? The three tricuspid valves at the entrance to the right ventricle are a hindrance to the return of blood into the vena cava. The three semilunar valves at the opening of the pulmonary artery are placed to prevent back flow of blood. Why, then, when there are similar structures in the left ventricle, should we deny them a similar purpose, of hindering at one place the escape, at the other the reflux of the blood?

2. When the size, shape, and position of these structures are almost the same in the left ventricle as in the right, why say they are for the purpose of impeding the escape and reflux of spirits in the left ventricle but of blood in the right? The same arrangement cannot be suited to hinder in a similar way blood as well as spirits.

3. When the openings and vessels mutually correspond in size, as is clear in the pulmonary artery and pulmonary vein,[10] why should one have a particular function, viz., of nourishing the lungs, but the other a general function?

---

[10] These terms in the Latin are confusing. The pulmonary artery was called *vena arteriosa*, "the vein similar to an artery." A "vein," because it carried "natural spirits" to nourish the lung, but its structure was recognized to be like that of the aorta, or great artery. The pulmonary vein was called *arteria venosa*, "the artery similar to a vein." An "artery" because it carried "vital spirits" (and many other things, as Harvey shows, in opposite directions!), but its structure was admittedly venous. It is not always easy to keep these terms straight. Even Dr. Robert Willis, whose splendid translation of Harvey for the Sydenham Society (1847) is the standard English version, slipped.

4. How is it possible (as Realdus Columbus notes) that so much blood is needed for the nourishment of the lungs, with the pulmonary artery leading to them exceeding in size both iliac veins?

5. Again I ask, when the lungs are so near, the blood vessel to them of such size, and themselves in continual motion, what is the object of the beat of the right ventricle? And why did Nature have to add this other ventricle to the heart for the sake of nourishing the lungs?

It is said that the left ventricle draws material for forming spirits, namely air and blood, from the lungs and right cavity of the heart. Likewise it sends spiritous blood into the aorta. From this it separates waste-vapors which are released to the lung by the pulmonary artery. From the lung spirits are obtained for the aorta. How is this separation made? How do spirits and waste-vapors pass here and there without mixture or confusion? If the mitral valves[11] do not stop the passage of waste

---

[11] These are referred to as *tricuspides mitrales*, and later in this same paragraph simply as *tricuspides*. The tricuspids and mitral valves are described in Chapter XVII, but not specifically differentiated by name. The specific terminology became established within the next century. Thus William Cheselden (1688–1752), in his *Anatomy of the Human Body*, 1713, says, "Over the entrance of the auricles in each ventricle, are placed valves to hinder a return of blood when the heart contracts. Those in the right ventricle are named Tricuspides, those in the left Mitrales." Harvey was not the first to use the term "mitral." Vesalius (1514–1564) was apparently the first to compare the left auriculoventricular valves to an episcopal miter. The best publication on the heart closely following Harvey's is Richard Lower's (1631–1690) *Tractatus de Corde* (London, 1669, translated by K. J. Franklin in

vapor to the lungs, how do they stop the escape of air? How do the semilunars prevent the return of spirits from the aorta following cardiac diastole? Above all, how can it be said that the pulmonary vein distributes the spiritous blood from the left ventricle to the lungs without hindrance from the mitral valves, having asserted that air enters the left ventricle from the lungs by this same vessel and is prevented from going back to the lungs by these same mitrals? Good God! How do the mitral valves prevent escape of air and not of blood?

Further, if the pulmonary artery, a large vessel, with heavy arterial walls, be destined for only the single particular purpose of nourishing the lungs, why should the pulmonary vein, scarcely of the same size, with soft flabby venous walls, be supposed to have three or four different uses? It is desired that air pass through this vessel from the lungs to the left ventricle, likewise that waste vapors escape by the same vessel from the heart to the lungs, and that some of the spiritous blood from the heart be distributed by it to keep the lungs alive.

To desire that waste vapors from the heart and air to the heart be transmitted by this same conduit is opposed to Nature which nowhere has made but

---

Vol. 9 of R. T. Gunther's *Early Science in Oxford*, Oxford, 1932). In this he specifically and consistently refers to the "mitral valves." Lower's work is fully discussed by K. J. Franklin (*Proc. Roy. Soc. Med.*, 25, Sect. Hist. Med., 7, 1931), and C. C. and P. M. Hoff (*Bull. Inst. Hist. Med.*, 4:517, 1936).

a single vessel or way for such contrary movements and purposes.

If waste vapors and air come and go by this passage, as they do in the pulmonary bronchi, why do we find neither air nor sooty vapors when we cut open the pulmonary vein? Why do we always find the pulmonary vein full of thick blood, never of air, while in the lungs we note plenty of air?

If one repeats Galen's experiment of opening the trachea of a living dog, forcing air into the lungs by a bellows, and then firmly tying off the trachea, a great abundance of air even out to the pleurae will be found in the lungs on opening the chest. No air, however, will be found in the pulmonary vein or in the left ventricle of the heart. It certainly should be if the heart drew in air from the lungs, or if the lungs transmitted air to the heart, in the living dog. On inflating the lungs of a cadaver in an anatomical demonstration, who doubts the air could be seen going this way if such a passage exists? This function of the pulmonary vein, the transmission of air from the lungs to the heart, is considered so significant that Hieronymus Fabricius of Aquapendente insists the lungs were made for the sake of this vessel[12] and that it is their most important structure.

I would like to know why the pulmonary vein is

----

[12] Not quite as respectful of Fabricius (1537–1619) as one would expect in a devoted pupil. For a translation of the passage referred to (De Respiratione, 1603), see M. Foster's famous History of Physiology, Cambridge, 1901, p. 38.

built like a vein if it is destined for the transmission of air.

It would be more natural for it to be made of ringed tubes such as those of the bronchi, in order always to be open and not liable to collapse. Thus it might remain free from blood with no liquid to hinder the passage of air, as may sometimes be noted in the lungs when they labor under more or less phlegm in the bronchi, when breathing is sibilant or strepitous.

Even less tolerable is the opinion which supposes two materials, air and blood, necessary for the formation of vital spirits. The blood is supposed to ooze through tiny pores in the septum of the heart[13] from the right to the left ventricle, while the air is drawn from the lungs by the large pulmonary vein. According to this many little openings exist in the septum of the heart suited to the passage of blood. But,

---

[13] Could these famous "pores in the septum" of Galenical physiology, imperfectly pictured by Leonardo, conservatively discussed by Vesalius, and scorned by Harvey, really have been what we now call the "Thebesian vessels," noted by R. Vieussens (*Nouvelle decouvertes sur le coeur*, Toulouse, 1706) and properly described by A. C. Thebesius (*Dissertatio medica de circulo sanguinis in corde*, Lug. Bat., 1708)? Anatomically, the orifices of the Thebesian canals with portions of the vessels arising from them may be seen with the unaided eye in the endocardium, along with the openings of intertrabecular spaces with which they may be confused (R. T. Grant and L. E. Viko, *Heart*, 15: 103, 1929). The Galenical error may indeed have been one of interpretation and not of observation. Galen's statements appear in his work entitled *On the Natural Faculties* (Bk. III, Chap. 15), translated and annotated by A. J. Brock (*Galen on the Natural Faculties*, Lond. and New York, 1916). This volume gives an admirable survey of Galenical physiology.

damn it, no such pores exist, nor can they be demonstrated!

The septum of the heart is of denser and more compact material than any part of the body except bones and tendons. Even so, supposing the pores are there, how could the left ventricle draw blood from the right when both ventricles contract and dilate at the same time? Why not rather believe that the right ventricle draws spirits through these pores from the left instead of the left ventricle drawing blood from the right? It is surely miraculous and incongruous that plenty of blood should be drawn through obscure invisible openings in the same time as air through wide open ones. Why require invisible pores and obscure uncertain channels to get the blood to the left ventricle when there is such a wide open passage through the pulmonary vein? It is certainly remarkable that a way had to be made, or rather invented, through the dense, tough, and compact septum of the heart, instead of through the open pulmonary vein, and the soft spongy mass of the lungs. If the blood can permeate the material of the septum, or be imbibed from the ventricles, what is the use of the coronary arteries and veins, branches of which go to the septum itself, for its nourishment?[14] Specially noteworthy

---

[14] Were these "branches" Harvey's interpretation of the Thebesian vessels? See note 10 for references. The Thebesian vessels communicate with the coronary veins and arteries. F. H. Pratt (Amer. J. Physiol., 1: 86, 1898) showed that these vessels may adequately nourish a perfused heart for a long time, and J. T. Wearn (J. Exper. Med.,

is this: if in the fetus, where everything is softer and more lax, Nature had to bring the blood to the left ventricle by the foramen ovale, from the vena cava through the pulmonary vein, how is it likely in the adult to pass so plentiously and with no effort through the cardiac septum, now denser with age? On the authority of Galen (*de loc. affect. lib. 6, cap.* 7), and the experience of Hollerius, Andreas Laurentius (*lib. 9, cap. 11, questione 12*) asserts that the serum and pus in empyema, absorbed from the thoracic cavity into the pulmonary vein, can be eliminated through the left ventricle of the heart and the arteries in the urine and feces. As evidence he cites a certain case of melancholy, who suffering from fainting spells, was relieved from the seizures by voiding some turbid and fetid urine. Worn out by the disease he finally died. On opening the body none of the material he excreted was found in the bladder or kidneys. In the left heart, however, and in the thoracic cavity, there was much of it, and Laurentius boasts he predicted the cause of the symptoms. I wonder, since he predicted that such conglomerate material was evacuated as indicated,[15] why he could not, or would not discern

---

47:293, 1928) confirmed this even in the event of gradual closure of the coronary orifices.

[15] How much of this is sarcasm against the pathology? Jacob Hollerius lived between 1498 and 1562. Andreas Laurentius (1550–1609) migrated from Montpellier to Paris, and although physician to Henry IV, was considered an ignorant man. His *Historia Anatomica Humani Corporis* was published in Frankfurt in 1602.

that the blood is naturally carried from the lungs to the left ventricle in the same way.

From these and many other considerations it is clear that what has so far been said on the movement and function of the heart and arteries must seem obscure, inconsistent, or impossible to the thoughtful student. It will therefore be proper to investigate the matter more closely, to study the movement of the heart and arteries not only in man but in all animals possessing a heart, and to search out and find the truth by frequent experiments in living animals, and by constant observation.

CHAPTER I

The Author's Reasons for Writing

WHEN I first tried animal experimentation for the purpose of discovering the motions and functions of the heart by actual inspection and not by other people's books, I found it so truly difficult that I almost believed with Fracastorius,[1] that the motion of the heart was to be understood by God alone. I could not really tell when systole or diastole took place, or when and where dilatation or constriction occurred, because of the quickness of the movement. In many animals this takes place in the twinkling of an eye, like a flash of lightning. Systole seemed at one time here, diastole there, then all reversed, varied and confused. So I could reach no decision, neither about what I might conclude myself nor believe from others. I did not marvel that Andreas Laurentius wrote that the motion of the heart was as perplexing as the flux and reflux of Euripus[2] was to Aristotle.

---

[1] *De sympathia et antipathia, Cap. 15, Opera Omnia,* Venice, 1555 p. 95. H. Fracastorius (1484–1553) was the author of the famous poem, *Syphilis sive Morbus Gallicus* (Verona, 1530), which gave the name to the disease syphilis.

[2] A narrow channel 113 miles long, between Euboea and Boeotia, opposite Chalcis, renowned in antiquity for the violent flow and reflow of its tide.

Finally, using greater care every day, with very frequent experimentation, observing a variety of animals, and comparing many observations, I felt my way out of this labyrinth, and gained accurate information, which I desired, of the motions and functions of the heart and arteries. From that time I have not hesitated to declare my thoughts on this matter, not only in private to friends, but even publicly in my anatomical lectures, as in the ancient Academy. As usual, these views pleased some, not others. Some blamed me of wrong in daring to depart from the precepts and faith of all anatomists. Others wanted more information on these new ideas which were thought worthy of interest and of possible value. Finally I have consented to the requests of friends, that anyone may be made acquainted with my work. I have also been moved by the envy of some who, receiving my words blindly and with no understanding, have tried to ridicule me in public. So I have decided to publish my findings so all may form an opinion of me and of the work itself. I am pleased to do this since Hieronymus Fabricius of Aquapendente, although he has correctly and in a scholarly manner described almost all the parts of animals, has not discussed the heart.

Finally, if my work may be helpful to this phase of literature, it may perhaps be granted that I have not lived idly. As the old man in the comedy says:[3]

---

[3] Terrence, in *Adelphi*, Act V, Sc. IV, 1 (Demea). Harvey quotes the Latin quite correctly. My unsatisfactory translation of the four

> None age so perfectly that subtle change
> With time or custom seems not new nor strange;
> What's once believed is now denied, and what
> Was honored once now suffers in exchange.

So may it now be regarding the motion of the heart. The path is open for others, starting here, to progress more fortunately and more correctly under a more propitious genius.

---

lines may be excused on the plea that it places the context in the appropriately tolerant and resigned verse-form made famous by Edward FitzGerald. Dr. Willis, in his 1847 Harvey, translates the lines in the classical tradition:

> For never yet hath any one attained
> To such perfection, but that time, and place,
> And use, have brought addition to his knowledge;
> Or made correction, or admonished him
> That he was ignorant of much which he
> Had thought he knew; or led him to reject
> What he had once esteemed of highest price.

George Colman's translation is quoted by T. B. Harbottle, *Dictionary of Quotations* (Classical), London and New York, 1897.

CHAPTER II

The Motions of the Heart as Observed in Animal Experiments

-+-━━■>●<■━━-+-

IN THE first place, when the chest of a living animal is opened, and the capsule surrounding the heart is cut away,[1] one may see that the heart alternates in movement and rest. There is a time when it moves, and a time when it is quiet.

This is more easily seen in the hearts of cold-blooded animals, as toads, snakes, frogs, snails, shell-fish, crustaceans, and fish. It is also more apparent in other animals as the dog and pig, if one carefully observes the heart as it moves more slowly when about to die. The movements then become slower and weaker and the pauses longer, so that it is easy to see what the motion really is and how made. During a pause, the heart is soft, flaccid, exhausted, as in death.

Three significant features are to be noted in the motion and in the period of movement:

---

[1] The only reference to the pericardium made by Harvey. The idea that it prevents overdistention of the heart probably never occurred to him. For current ideas on the function of the pericardium see J. A. Wilson and W. J. Meek, Amer. J. Physiol., 82: 34 (Sept.) 1927, and C. J. Wiggers, *Physiology in Health and Disease*, 3rd Ed., Phila., 1939, p. 675.

1. The heart is lifted, and rises up to the apex, so that it strikes the chest at that moment, and the beat may be felt on the outside.[2]

2. It contracts all over, but particularly to the sides, so that it looks narrower and longer. An isolated eel's heart placed on a table or in the hand shows this well, but it may also be seen in the hearts of fishes and of cold-blooded animals in which the heart is conical or lengthened.

3. Grasping the heart in the hand, it feels harder when it moves. This hardness is due to tension, as when one grasps the fore-arm and feels its tendons become knotty when the fingers are moved.

4. An additional point may be noted in fishes and cold-blooded animals, as serpents and frogs. When the heart moves it is paler in color, but when it pauses it is of a deeper blood color.

---

[2] The first clear statement of the significance of the apex beat. In the physiological analysis of the events of the cardiac cycle in an intact subject, this is an important reference point, marking, as Harvey noted, the moment of ventricular systole and emptying. The graphic analysis of the cardiac cycle was especially developed by E. J. Marey (1830–1904), *La Circulation du Sang*, Paris, 1881, and was made possible by the methods of recording by kymograph initiated by Carl Ludwig (1816–1895).

This is the first of that remarkable series of extraordinarily acute observations on the motion of the heart and blood so simply and clearly reported by Harvey in this book. Compare the number and quality of these observations and the clear interpretation of their significance as made by him, with the stumbling, vague, and incomplete ideas on the matter as given by Servetus (1510–1553), Columbus (1516–1559), Ruini (died before 1598), Caesalpinus (1524–1603), and others for whom credit is claimed for discovering the circulation, and you will agree that to Harvey alone should be given the honor of first realizing the full truth, and of demonstrating it to the world.

From these facts it seems clear to me that the motion of the heart consists of a tightening all over, both contraction along the fibers, and constriction everywhere. In its movement it becomes erect, hard, and smaller. The motion is just the same as that of muscles when contracting along their tendons and fibers. The muscles in action become tense and tough, and lose their softness in becoming hard, while they thicken and stand out.[3] The heart acts similarly.

From these points it is reasonable to conclude that the heart at the moment it acts, becomes constricted all over, thicker in its walls and smaller in its ventricles, in order to expel its content of blood. This is clear from the fourth observation above in which it was noted that the heart becomes pale when it squeezes the blood out during contraction, but when quiet in relaxation the deep blood red color returns as the ventricle fills again with blood. But

---

[3] Niels Stensen (1638–1686), the Danish anatomist who later became a bishop of the Roman church, is usually credited with recognizing the muscular character of the heart (*De Musculis et Glandulis Observationum Specimen*, 1664). This is a little unfair to Harvey, and, for that matter, to the unknown author of the Hippocratic tract on the heart to which Harvey refers in Chapter XVII. Stensen, as far as I can determine, did little more than these in comparing the heart's contraction to that of a muscle, and then saying that it is nothing more than muscle. The structural (histological) similarity between the heart and muscle was shown in A. Leeuwenhoek's (1632–1723) *Arcana Naturae* (Delft, 1695), in which *Epistola 82* (page 445) gives the first clear account of the peculiar structure of cardiac muscle, with excellent illustrations. For an interesting account of Stensen, see Dr. W. S. Miller's paper, Johns Hopkins Hosp. Bull., 25: 44 (Feb.) 1914.

no one need doubt further, for if the cavity of the ventricle be cut into, the blood contained therein will be forcibly squirted out when the heart is tense with each movement or beat.

The following things take place, then, simultaneously: the contraction of the heart; the beat at the apex against the chest, which may be felt outside; the thickening of the walls; and the forcible ejection of the blood it contains by the constriction of the ventricles.

So the opposite of the commonly received opinion seems true. Instead of the heart opening its ventricles and filling with blood at the moment it strikes the chest and its beat is felt on the outside, the contrary takes place so that the heart while contracting empties. Therefore the motion commonly thought the diastole of the heart is really the systole, and the significant movement of the heart is not the diastole but the systole. The heart does not act in diastole but in systole for only when it contracts is it active.

It is not to be admitted that the heart moves only in the direction of its straight fibers. The great Vesalius, in support of this idea, speaks of a bundle of willow-twigs bound in a pyramid.[4] It is implied that as the apex is drawn to the base, the sides

---

[4] Andreas Vesalius (1514-1564), *De Humani Corporis Fabrica*, Basle, 1543, *Lib. 6, Cap. 10*, p. 587. It is interesting to note how Vesalius described fairly well the gross structures of the heart, and then fitted them as best he could into the Galenical system.

bulge outward, the cavities dilate, the ventricles take the shape of cupping glasses, and suck the blood into them. But all the fibers constrict the heart at the same time that they make it tense, thus thickening the walls and substance rather than enlarging the ventricles. As the fibers stretch from the apex to the base of the heart, drawing the apex toward the base, they do not tend to make the walls bulge outwards, but rather the reverse, for all fibers spirally arranged become straight on contraction. This is true of all muscular fibers. When they contract they shorten longitudinally and distend sidewise as they thicken, as noted in the bellies of muscles generally. To this may be added that the ventricles are not constricted only by virtue of the direction and thickening of their walls. The walls contain solely circular fibers, but there are also bands containing only straight fibers, which are noted in the ventricles of larger animals and which are called nerves by Aristotle.[5] When they contract

---

[5] The inside walls of the ventricles are ridged with many projecting bands of muscle tissue, arranged as (1) separate threads stretched across the cavity, the *moderator bands* especially noted in the right ventricle; (2) columns on the walls, the *columnae carneae*, which are probably referred to here, and (3) small elevations on the walls, *papillary muscles*, which are prolonged in the *chordae tendineae* extending to the valves. The latter probably aid in closing more exactly the valve flaps. See R. Burton-Opitz's *Physiology*, Phila. and London, 1920, p. 267–270. Harvey discusses these "bands" again in Chapter XVII. Harvey's many references to Aristotle indicate his extensive knowledge of and his dependence on Aristotle's writings. These are available in the excellent Oxford translations (*The Parva Naturalia* by J. I. Beare and G. R. T. Ross, Oxford, 1908; *Historia Animalium* by

together an excellent system is present to pull the internal surfaces closely together, as with cords, in order to eject the blood with greater force.

Likewise, it is not true, as commonly believed, that the heart by its own action or distention draws blood into its ventricles. When it moves and contracts it expels blood, when it relaxes and is quiet it receives blood in the manner soon to be described.

D. W. Thompson, Oxford, 1910; *De Generatione Animalium*, by A. Platt, Oxford, 1910; and *De Partibus Animalium* by W. Ogle, Oxford, 1911).

CHAPTER III

The Movements of the Arteries as Seen in Animal Experimentation

IN CONNECTION with the movements of the heart one may observe these facts regarding the movements and pulses of the arteries:

1. At the instant the heart contracts, in systole, and strikes the breast, the arteries dilate, give a pulsation, and are distended. Also, when the right ventricle contracts and expels its content of blood, the pulmonary artery beats and is dilated along with the other arteries of the body.

2. When the left ventricle stops beating or contracting, the pulsations in the arteries cease, or the contractions being weak, the pulse in the arteries is scarcely perceptible. A similar cessation of the pulse in the pulmonary artery occurs when the right ventricle stops.

3. If any artery be cut or punctured, the blood spurts forcibly from the wound when the left ventricle contracts. Likewise, if the pulmonary artery is cut, blood vigorously squirts out when the right ventricle contracts.

In fishes, also, if the blood vessel leading from the heart to the gills is cut open, the blood will be seen to spurt out when the heart contracts.

Finally, in arteriotomy, the blood is seen squirted alternately far and near, the greater spurt coming with the distention of the artery, at the time the heart strikes the ribs. This is the moment the heart contracts and is in systole, and it is by this motion that the blood is ejected.

Contrary to the usual teaching, it is clear from the facts, that the diastole of the arteries corresponds to the systole of the heart, and that the arteries are filled and distended by the blood forced into them by the contraction of the ventricles. The arteries are distended because they are filled like sacs, not because they expand like bellows. All the arteries of the body pulsate because of the same cause, the contraction of the left ventricle. Likewise the pulmonary artery pulsates because of the contraction of the right ventricle.

To illustrate how the beat in the arteries is due to the impulse of blood from the left ventricle, one may blow into a glove, distending all the fingers at one and the same time, like the pulse. The pulse corresponds to the tension of the heart in frequency, rhythm, volume, and regularity. Because of the motion of the blood it is reasonable to expect the heart beat and the dilatation of the arteries, even the more distant ones, to go together.[1] It is like inflating

---

[1] Rather interesting that Harvey should have avoided the idea of a transmission of the pulse-wave, especially since in Chapter 5 he discusses the transmission of the wave of contraction over the heart itself. Did he attempt to time with the inadequate instruments of his day the apex beat and say the pulse at the wrist? It is rather a broad conclusion

a glove or bladder, or like in a drum or long beam, when the stroke and beat occur together, even at the extremities. Aristotle says (*De Animal. 3, Cap. 9*), "*The blood of all animals throbs in the veins* (arteries are meant), *and by the pulse is sent everywhere at once.*" And again (*De Respirat. Cap. 15*), "*All veins pulsate together intermittently, because they all depend on the heart. As it is always in intermittent movement, so they move together, intermittently.*" It is to be noted, according to Galen (*De Plac. Hippocr. & Plat., Cap. 9*), that the ancient philosophers referred to the arteries as veins.

I once had a case in charge which convinced me of this truth. This person had a large pulsating tumor, called an aneurysm, on the right neck where the subclavian artery descends toward the axilla. Caused

to reach, that the pulse corresponds in all particulars to the heart beat, and it is reasonable to believe Harvey studied and pondered over the problem for a long time.

Erasistratus noted that the pulse progresses as a wave, but this was denied by Galen. Both Albrecht von Haller (1708–1777), *Elementa Physiologiae* 1757, tom. 1, p. 447, and M.-F.-Xavier Bichat (1771–1802), agreed with Harvey that the pulse is synchronous in all the arteries. Ernst Heinrich Weber (1795–1878) in 1827 first showed a delay in transmission. From his observations, first printed in his *Pulsum arteriarum*, Leipzig, 1827, one may calculate the velocity of the pulse-wave to be 9.2 meters per second, and its length 3 meters. More recent determinations of the velocity show it to be somewhat slower (see W. H. Howell's splendid *Physiology*, 14th Ed., Phila., 1940, p. 519). For an authoritative appreciation of E. H. Weber, consult P. M. Dawson's delightful account in the William Snow Miller *Festschrift*. The velocity of blood-flow, in a given vessel, an entirely different proposition, was carefully investigated by Carl Ludwig (1816–1895). For a discussion of the velocity of blood flow consult C. J. Wiggers' *Physiology in Health and Disease*, 3rd Ed., Phila., 1939, p. 542.

by the erosion of the artery itself, it was daily getting larger, and was distended with each pulsation by the rush of blood from the artery. Post mortem examination showed the relation of the parts. The pulse in this same arm was small because the greater part of the blood to it was intercepted by the tumor.

Wherever the motion of the blood in the arteries is impeded, by compression, by infarction, or by interception, there is less pulsation distally,[2] since the beat of the arteries is nothing else than the impulse of blood in these vessels.

---

[2] It is remarkable that the clinical applications of Harvey's work were so long neglected. Here and later he clearly indicates how his views may aid in diagnosis, treatment, and prognosis. The practicing physicians, however, would have none of it. Even some manuscript notes of Wm. Cullen's (1712–1790) lectures on the *Practice of Physic*, over a century later, only refer casually to the use of Dr. Harvey's observations on the control of hemorrhage. It may be that the practical success of Thomas Sydenham (1624–1689) as a physician focused attention on the neat pigeon-holing scheme of his classification of disease by symptoms (nosology), so that the applications of the new work in anatomy and physiology to medicine were overlooked.

CHAPTER IV

The Motion of the Heart and its Auricles as Noted in Animal Experimentation

—————◆▶◆◀◆——◆—

IN ADDITION to the motions of the heart already considered, those of the auricles are also to be discussed.

It has been reported by two skilled anatomists, Caspar Bauhin (*lib. 2, cap. 21*) and John Riolan[1] (*lib. 8, cap. 1*), that if the motions of the heart of a living animal are carefully watched, four movements distinct in time and place are to be seen, of which two belong to the auricles and two to the ventricles. In spite of these authorities, there are

---

[1] Caspar Bauhin (1560–1624) was Professor of Botany and Anatomy in Basle. His *Theatrum Anatomicum* (1605) is an unoriginal but reliable text. John Riolan (1577–1657) was generally regarded as the leading anatomist of his day. As Professor of Anatomy and Pharmacy, and Dean of the Medical Faculty of the University of Paris, he was an extremely influential conservative. On the basis of fairly reasonable arguments, he opposed Harvey's views on the circulation in his *Encheiridium Anatomicum* (1648), and *Opuscula Anatomica Nova* (1649). This was the only criticism against which Harvey deigned to reply, in his *Exercitationes duae anatomicae de circulatione sanguinis ad Jo. Riolanum* (1649). These are available in the beautiful English of Robert Willis' 1847 translations of Harvey's works for the Sydenham Society. For an admirable account of Riolan's views, see J. C. Dalton's scholarly *Doctrines of the Circulation*, Phila., 1884. Riolan's book, to which Harvey probably refers here, is his *Anthropographia* (1618).

not four movements distinct in time, but only in space. The two auricles beat together and so do the two ventricles, so that there are four distinct movements in space, but only two in time. This happens as follows.

Two sets of movements occur together, one of the auricles, another of the ventricles. These are not simultaneous, but that of auricles precedes that of the rest of the heart. The movement seems to start in the auricles and to spread to the ventricles.[2] When the heart slows in approaching death, or in fishes and cold-blooded animals, there is a pause between the two movements, and the heart seems to respond to the motion as if aroused, sometimes quickly, sometimes slowly. At length, nearly dead, it fails to respond to the motion, and it stirs so obscurely that the only signs of motion are pulsations of the auricle, as if just lightly nodding the head. The heart thus stops beating before the auricles, and the latter may be said to outlive it. The left ventricle stops beating first of all, then its auricle, then the right ventricle, and, finally, as indeed Galen noted, when all the rest is quiet and dead, the right auricle still pulsates. Life, therefore, seems to remain longest in the right auricle. While the heart gradually dies, it sometimes responds with a

---

[2] The first clear statement on the problem of the origin and conduction of the heart beat. For a recent comprehensive discussion of this question see J. A. E. Eyster and W. J. Meek, *Physiological Reviews*, 1: 1 (1921).

single weak and feeble beat to two or three pulsations of the auricles.[3]

With the auricles still pulsating after the heart has stopped, it is noteworthy that a finger placed on the ventricles perceives the separate pulsations of the auricles for the same reason as the beat of the ventricles in the arteries is felt, because, as was

---

[3] The first observation of heart-block. The great Haller (1708–1777) later postulated a peristaltic muscular wave from the vena cava to the aorta over the heart, but Moritz Schiff (1823–1896), by noting again what Harvey had observed in the dying heart, showed this concept untenable. The term "heart-block" was introduced by W. H. Gaskell (1847–1914), in his masterful analysis of the heart beat (Phil. Tr., Lond., 173: 933, 1882) which soundly established the "myogenic" theory of the movement. In this treatise "it is shown that the motor influences from the nerve ganglia in the sinus venosus influence the rhythm (rate and force) of the heart, but do not originate its movements or beat, which are due to the automatic rhythmic contractile power of the heart muscle itself and to the peristaltic contraction wave which proceeds from sinus venosus to bulbus arteriosus and from muscle fiber to muscle fiber" (Garrison). Much of this may be deduced from Harvey's observations in this Chapter. Gaskell's studies were extended by T. W. Engelmann (1843–1909). They gave a new interpretation to the classical experiments of H. Stannius (1808–1883) who showed (Müller's Arch., 1852, 163) that a ligature around the sino-auricular junction would stop the heart, while a second ligature around the auricular-ventricular groove would be followed by slow ventricular beats. W. His, Jr., in 1893, found a thin strip of muscle between the auricles and ventricles, which according to Gaskell's ideas, serves as the conducting medium for the contractile impulses between auricles and ventricles. The clinical significance of heart-block or Stokes-Adams disease was first emphasized by R. Adams (1791–1875) in the Dublin Hospital Reports, 4: 396, 1827, and by W. Stokes (1804–1878) in the Dublin Quarterly Journal of Medical Science, 2: 73, 1846. The clinical study of these phenomena has been greatly facilitated by electrocardiographic methods developed chiefly by W. Einthoven (K. Acad. Amster. Proc. Sect. Sc., 6: 107, 1903). For clinical discussion see Sir Thomas Lewis' *The Mechanism and Graphic Registration of the Heart Beat*, 3rd Ed., London, 1925, and A. R. Barnes' *Electrocardiographic Patterns*, Springfield, Ill., 1940.

said before, of the distention from the impact of blood. At this same time when the auricles alone are beating, if you cut off the tip of the heart with a scissors, you will see blood gush out at each beat of the auricles. This shows how blood enters the ventricles, not by the suction or dilatation of the ventricles, but by the beat of the auricles.

Note that when I speak of the pulsations of the auricles or of the heart, I mean contractions. First the auricles contract, then afterwards the heart itself. When the auricles contract they become pale, especially when they hold little blood (for they are filled as reservoirs, the blood freely pressing toward them through the veins).[4] This whiteness is most apparent near their edges when they contract.

In fishes, frogs and other animals having a

---

[4] The first intimation of the existence of venous pressure. A more literal translation would read "freely tending by the compressing motion of the veins." While the veins are not now considered to exert much elastic pressure, it is taught that muscular activity exerts pressure on the veins. Harvey discusses the functions of the venous valves in Chapter 13. There is little emphasis in current physiological texts on auricular contraction filling the ventricles, although careful investigators estimate that between 18 and 60 per cent of the blood content of the ventricles is forced in by auricular contraction (C. J. Wiggers, *The Circulation in Health and Disease*, Phila., 2nd Ed., 1923.) The current opinion is that venous pressure largely determines the diastolic filling. But W. Hamilton gives evidence that little or no blood flows to the heart in diastole, while an amount nearly equal to the systolic discharge enters the auricles during ventricular systole (Amer. J. Physiol., 91: 712, 1930). For a review of venous pressure see J. Eyster, Physiol. Rev., 6: 281, 1926. For a comprehensive survey of the physiology of veins, consult K. J. Franklin's *A Monograph on Veins*, Springfield, Ill., 1937.

single ventricle in the heart, at the base of which the auricle is swollen like a bladder with blood, you may see this bladder contract first, plainly followed afterwards by the contraction of the rest of the heart.

It is only fair to report what I have observed to the contrary. The heart of an eel, of certain fishes, and even of other animals, may beat without the auricles. Even if it is cut in pieces, the separate parts may be seen to contract and relax.[5] So even after auricular movement has stopped, the body of the heart may beat and pulsate. But may not this be characteristic of those animals more tenacious of life, whose basic humor is more glutinous or sluggish, and not easily dissipated? The same thing is noted in the flesh of eels, which continues to wriggle even after skinning and slicing in pieces.

In an experiment one time on a pigeon, after the heart had stopped, and even after the auricles were motionless for some time, I placed my finger, warm and kept wet with saliva, upon the heart. By this warm application it recovered life and strength, the auricles and ventricles beat, alternately contracting and relaxing, apparently recalled from death.[6]

---

[5] An astonishingly brief significant observation from which may be deduced the three fundamental and characteristic properties of cardiac muscle: automaticity, contractility, and rhythmicity.

[6] The first recorded "perfusion" of an isolated heart, again demonstrating the basic properties of cardiac muscle. Only an Englishman could append at that time the last phrase of this paragraph without

Besides this I have sometimes noticed, after the heart and even the right auricle had completely stopped beating, that a slight motion or palpitation remained in the blood in the right auricle, as long as it seemed imbued with heat and spirit. Something similar is very apparent in embryology, as may be seen during the first seven days of the hatching of a hen's egg. First, before anything else, a drop of blood appears, which throbs, as Aristotle had noted. From this, with increasing growth and formation of the chick, the auricles of the heart are made, in the pulsations of which there is continual evidence of life. After a few more days, when the body is outlined, the rest of the heart is made, but for some time it remains pale and bloodless like the rest of the body, and does not throb. I have seen a similar condition in a human embryo about the beginning of the third month, the ventricles being pale and bloodless, but the auricles containing some purple blood. In the egg, when the fetus forms and develops, the heart grows also and acquires ventricles, with which blood is received and transmitted.

Whoever examines this matter closely will not say that the heart entirely is the first to live and the last to die, but rather the auricles (or that part corresponding to the auricles in serpents, fishes, and such animals) which live before the rest of the heart, and die after it.

---

thought of its theological consequences. Galileo was forced to renounce his scientific ideas before a Papal tribunal in 1632, and in Germany the horrible Thirty Years War was in full swing.

I should say rather that the blood itself or spirit has in it an obscure throbbing which it seems to hold after death, and whether we may say that life begins with a cardiac palpitation is doubtful.[7] The seminal fluids or prolific spirit, of all animals, as Aristotle noted, goes forth with a bound, as if alive. Nature in death turns back, retracing her steps, as Aristotle says (*De Motu Animal., Cap. 8*), and comes again to the place from which she started. In the generation of life, what is not animal develops to animal, a non-entity to an entity, and by retrogression in corruption returns from an entity to a non-entity. So in animals what is made last dies first, what first dies last.

I have observed that there is a heart in almost all animals, not only in the larger ones with blood, as Aristotle claims, but in the smaller bloodless ones also, as snails, slugs, crabs, shrimps, and many

---

[7] One must admire the intellectual courage of Harvey in this sort of speculation. Aristotelian in the philosophical aspects of his work, Harvey is not here specifically attempting to locate the anatomical seat of the soul, although that is implied. His demonstration really stopped this vain search (H. M. Brown, Annals of Medical History, 5: 1, 1923).

Note through here not only the remarkable embryological observations (later developed in his *Exercitationes de generatione animalium*, 1651), but also the extraordinary remarks on invertebrate anatomy and physiology. These are the first of any significance since Aristotle, of whom surely Harvey was the first real disciple. Both P. Belon (1517-1564) and G. Rondelet (1509-1566)—Rabelais' "*Rondibilis*," wrote valuable texts on fishes, 1551 and 1554, but they did not discuss lower forms. In the last paragraph of this Chapter, one may sense the wonder and awe Harvey must have felt as he pondered on what he saw.

others. Even in wasps, hornets, and flies, have I seen with a lens a beating heart at the upper part of what is called a tail, and I have shown it living to others.

In these bloodless animals the heart beats slowly, contracting sluggishly as in moribund higher animals. This is easily seen in the snail, where the heart lies at the bottom of that opening on the right side which seems to open and close as saliva is expelled. The incision should be made on the top of the body near the part corresponding to the liver.

It is to be noted that in winter and cold seasons, the bloodless animals, as the snail, show no pulsation. They seem to live like vegetables or those things called plant-animals.

It is also to be noted that an auricle or its analogue is present in all animals possessing a heart, and where there is a double ventricle, there are always two auricles, but not the reverse. But turning to the development of the chick in the egg, there is, as I said, only a vesicle or auricle, at first, or a throbbing drop of blood, which, as growth progresses, becomes the heart. So in some animals, not reaching the highest organization, as bees, wasps, snails, shrimps, and craw-fish, there is a throbbing vesicle or an alternately red and white point, as the mainstay of life.

There is a small squid, called a *shrimp* in English, *een gerneel* in Flemish, which is caught at sea and in the Thames, whose entire body is transparent.

Placing this creature in water, I have often shown some of my friends the movements of its heart with great clearness. Since the outside of the body did not block our view, we could observe the least tremor of the heart, as through a window.

I have seen the first rudiments of the chick as a little cloud in the hen's egg about the fourth or fifth day of incubation, with the shell removed and the egg placed in clear warm water. In the center of the cloud there was a throbbing point of blood, so trifling that it disappeared on contraction and was lost to sight, while on relaxation it appeared again like a red pin-point. Throbbing between existence and non-existence, now visible, now invisible, it was the beginning of life.

CHAPTER V

The Actions and Functions of the Heart

--→--■>●<●──+--

FROM these and other observations I am convinced that the motion of the heart is as follows:

First, the auricle contracts, and this forces the abundant blood it contains as the cistern and reservoir of the veins, into the ventricle. This being filled, the heart raises itself, makes its fibers tense, contracts, and beats. By this beat it at once ejects into the arteries the blood received from the auricle; the right ventricle sending its blood to the lungs through the vessel called the *vena arteriosa,* but which in structure and function is an artery; the left ventricle sending its blood to the aorta, and to the rest of the body through the arteries.

These two motions, one of the auricles, the other of the ventricles, are consecutive, with a rhythm between them,[1] so that only one movement may

---

[1] The auricular-ventricular rhythm has become an important subject for investigation and discussion since the introduction of electrocardiographic studies by means of W. Einthoven's (1860–1927) string galvanometer. See F. H. Garrison's *History of Medicine,* 4th Ed., Phila., 1929, p. 687.

Note the excellent description of the chain of events in the act of swallowing. Here is an example of that straight-forward mechanistic description of functional activity in which Harvey so closely approxi-

be apparent, especially in warm-blooded animals where it happens rapidly. This is like a piece of machinery in which one wheel moves another, though all seem to move simultaneously, or like the mechanism in fire-arms, where touching the trigger brings down the flint, lights a spark, which falls in the powder and explodes it, firing the ball, which reaches the mark. All these events because of their quickness seem to occur simultaneously in the twinking of an eye. Likewise in swallowing: lifting the tongue and pressing the mouth forces the food to the throat, the larynx and the epiglottis are closed by their own muscles, the gullet rises and opens its mouth like a sac, and receiving the bolus forces it down by its transverse and longitudinal muscles. All these diverse movements, carried out by different organs, are done so smoothly and regularly that they seem to be a single movement and action, which we call swallowing

So it happens in the movement and action of the heart, which is sort of a deglutition or transference of blood from the veins to the arteries. If anyone with these points in mind will carefully watch the cardiac action in a living animal, he will see, not only what I have said, that the heart contracts in a continuous movement with the auricles, but also a peculiar side-wise turning toward the right ventricle

mates the current attitude. The classical descriptions of deglutition are by F. Magendie (1783–1855), Précis élément. de Physiol., 2: 58, 1817, and by H. Kronecker (1839–1914) and S. J. Meltzer (1851–1921), Arch. f. Physiol., 1880, 299 and 446.

as if it twists slightly on itself in performing its work. It is easy to see when a horse drinks that water is drawn in and passed to the stomach with each gulp, the movement making a sound, and the pulsation may be heard and felt. So it is with each movement of the heart when a portion of the blood is transferred from the veins to the arteries, that a pulse is made which may be heard in the chest.[2]

The motion of the heart, then, is of this general type. The chief function of the heart is the transmission and pumping of the blood through the arteries to the extremities of the body. Thus the pulse which we feel in the arteries is nothing else than the impact of blood from the heart.

Whether or not the heart, besides transferring, distributing and giving motion to the blood, adds anything else to it, as heat, spirits, or perfection, may be discussed later and determined on other grounds. It is enough now to have shown that during the heart beat the blood is transferred through the ventricles from the veins to the arteries, and distributed to the whole body.

This much may be generally admitted on the basis of the structure of the heart and the position and

---

[2] One of the first observations of heart-sounds. An interpretation of their significance together with clinical application was made by R.-T.-H. Laënnec (1781-1826) in his epochal *Traité de l'auscultation médiate* (1819). See W. H. Howell's *Physiology*, 14th Ed., Phila., 1940, p. 550, and O. Orias and E. Braun-Menéndez's *The Heart Sounds in Normal and Pathological Conditions*, Oxford, 1939. For a history of knowledge of heart sounds, Garrison refers to G. Joseph, Janus, 2: 1, 345, 565, 1853.

action of its valves. But contradictory and incoherent statements are made about the matter by some who stumble around in the dark, saying much on conjecture only, as has been pointed out before.

The chief cause of perplexity and error in this matter seems to me to be the close connection between the heart and lungs in man. When the so-called venous artery, and arterial vein, were both seen to disappear into the lungs, it was very puzzling to determine how the right ventricle might distribute blood to the body or the left draw blood from the vena cava. This was implied by Galen in controverting Erasistratus on the origin and function of the veins, and the formation of blood (*De Placit. Hippocrat. & Plat.*, cap. 6), "*You will reply that this is true, that the blood is made in the liver, and then carried to the heart to receive its correct form and full perfection. This is not unreasonable, no great or perfect work is finished at one effort, nor can it get its whole polish from one tool. But if this is really so, show us another vessel which takes the perfect blood from the heart, and distributes it, as the arteries do the spirits, to the whole body.*" Thus Galen would not consent to a reasonable opinion, because not seeing a way of transit, he could not discover a vessel to spread the blood from the heart to the whole body!

I wonder what that great and ingenious man would have replied, had someone appeared for Erasistratus, or for that opinion now held by us and admitted to be reasonable by Galen himself, and had then pointed to the aorta as the vessel for distributing blood from the heart to the rest of the body? Had he said this transmits spirits and not blood, he would have sufficiently answered Erasistratus, who thought the arteries contained spirits alone. But he would have thus contradicted himself, and basely denied what he had strongly argued in his writings against this same Erasistratus, in showing by many potent reasons and by experiment that the arteries contain blood and not spirits.

The great man often agrees in this connection that "*all arteries arise from the aorta, and this from the heart, all normally containing and carrying blood.*" He says further, "*The three semilunar valves, placed at the opening of the aorta, prevent the reflux of blood into the heart. Nature would never have connected them with such an important organ unless for some great purpose.*" If the "Prince of Physicians" admits all this, as quoted in his very words from the book cited, I do not see how he can deny that the aorta is the very vessel to carry the blood, properly perfected, from the heart to the whole body. Does he hesitate, as all after him to the present, because he could not see on account of the close connection between heart and lungs, a way by which blood might go from veins to arteries?

This matter greatly bothered the anatomists. Always finding in dissection the pulmonary vein[3]

---

[3] This is one of the few places where a slip was made by Robert Willis, the great Sydenham Society translator of Harvey (1847). He

and the left ventricle filled with thick clotted blood, they were forced to say that blood oozed through the septum of the heart from the right ventricle to the left. I have already refuted this notion. A new path is to be found and described. This done, I believe there will be no more difficulty in agreeing with what I suggest about the beat of the heart and arteries, the transfer of blood from veins to arteries and its distribution to the body through the arteries.

---

calls the vessel the "pulmonary artery," and every editor of the translation has passed it by, when the context alone should raise a doubt. The text reads *arteriam venosam*, the artery like unto a vein, or the pulmonary vein.

CHAPTER VI

The Way by which the Blood Passes from the Vena Cava to the Arteries, or from the Right Ventricle of the Heart to the Left

——————

SINCE the close contact of the heart and lungs in man has probably been a source of error, as I have said, the common practice of anatomists, in dogmatizing on the general make-up of the animal body, from the dissections of dead human subjects alone, is objectionable. It is like devising a general system of politics, from the study of a single state, or deigning to know all agriculture from an examination of a single field. It is fallacious to attempt to draw general conclusions from one particular proposition.

If only anatomists were as familiar with the dissection of lower animals as with that of the human body, all these perplexing difficulties would, in my opinion, be cleared up.

The situation is first of all clear enough in fishes, where there is a single ventricle in the heart, and no lungs. The sac at the base of the heart, doubtless corresponding to the auricle, pushes the blood into the heart, which plainly transmits it by a tube analogous to an artery. This may be confirmed by inspection, or section of the artery, the blood spurting with each beat of the heart.

It is not hard to see the same thing in other animals with but a single ventricle, as toads, frogs, serpents and lizzards. They have lungs of a sort, as a voice. I have made notes on the excellent structure of their lungs, but they are not appropriate here. It is obvious in opening these animals that the blood is transferred from the veins to the arteries by the heart beat. The way is wide open; there is no difficulty or hesitancy about it; it is the same as it would be in man were the septum of the heart perforated or removed, making one ventricle of the two. Were this so, no one would doubt, I think, how blood passes from veins to arteries.

Since there really are more animals without lungs than with them, and also more with a single ventricle in the heart than with two, it may be concluded that for the majority of animals, an open way exists for blood to pass through the cavity of the heart from the veins to the arteries.

I have perceived further that the same thing is very apparent in the embryos of animals possessing lungs.

It is well known by all anatomists that the four blood vessels belonging to the heart, the vena cava, pulmonary artery, pulmonary vein, and aorta, are connected differently in the fetus than in the adult.

In the fetus a lateral anastomosis joins the vena cava to the pulmonary vein. This is located before the vena cava opens into the right ventricle of the heart, or gives off the coronary vein, just above its exit from the liver. This is a good-sized oval-shaped hole opening a passage from the vena cava to the pulmonary vein, so that blood may freely flow from the one to the other, then into the left auricle of the heart, and then to the left ventricle. In this *foramen ovale*, there is a thin tough membrane, larger than the opening, hanging like a cover from the pulmonary vein side. In the adult this blocks the foramen, and adhering on all sides, finally closes and obliterates it. In the fetus, however, this membrane hangs loosely, opening an easy way to the lungs and heart for the blood flowing from the vena cava, but at the same time blocking any passage back into that vein. In the embryo, one may conclude then that blood continually passes through this foramen from the vena cava to the pulmonary vein, and then into the left ventricle of the heart. After making this passage, it can not regurgitate.

Another junction is by the pulmonary artery where it divides into two branches after leaving the right ventricle. It is like a third trunk added to these two, a sort of arterial canal passing obliquely toward and perforating the aorta. Thus in dissecting a human embryo it appears as though there were two aortae or roots of the great artery rising from the heart.

This canal gradually shrinks after birth and is finally obliterated like the umbilical vessels.

There is no membrane in this arterial canal to impede the movement of the blood in either direction. At the entrance of the pulmonary artery, from which this canal extends, there are three sigmoid valves opening outwards, so the blood flows easily from the right ventricle into this vessel and the aorta, but by closing tightly they prevent any back flow from the arteries or lungs into the right ventricle. Thus when the heart contracts in the embryo, there is reason to believe the blood is continually propelled through this way from the right ventricle to the aorta.

It is commonly said that these two great junctions are for the nourishing of the lungs. This is improbable and inconsistent, since they are closed up and obliterated in the adult, although the lungs then, because of their heat and motion, must be thought to require more nourishment. It is also false to claim that Nature had to make these passages to nourish the lungs because the heart does not beat nor move in the embryo. Nature feels no such need, for in the hatching egg, and in the human embryo, removed quickly from the uterus at an autopsy, the heart beats just as in an adult. I am not alone in often seeing these movements, for Aristotle testifies (*Lib. de Spir.*, cap. *3*), "*Being part of the constitution of the heart, the pulse appears at its very beginning, as may be seen in animal experiments, and in the formation of the chick.*" These passages are not only open to the time of birth in man, and in certain animals, but even for many months in others, as anatomists have noted, and for years or life in still others, as in the goose, snipe, and many birds and small animals. This perhaps persuaded Botallus[1] that he had found a new passage for blood from the vena cava to the left ventricle. I confess I almost thought so myself when I first saw the condition in larger adult mice.

From this it appears that the same thing happens in human and other embryos in which these junctions are not closed: the heart, in its beat, forces the blood through the wide open passages from the vena cava to the aorta through the two ventricles. The right ventricle, receiving blood from its auricle, propels it through the pulmonary artery and its continuation, called the *ductus arteriosus*, to the aorta. At the same time the left ventricle contracts and sends into the aorta the blood, which, received from the beat of its auricle, has come through the foramen ovale from the vena cava.

In embryos, then, while the lungs are as inert and motionless as though not present, Nature uses for transmitting blood the two ventricles of the heart as if they were one. The situation is the same in embryos

---

[1] L. Bottallus, a French anatomist of little ability, was born about 1530. "His very imperfect description of the *ductus arteriosus*, which we know now to be due to the persistence of the fifth cephalic aortic arch on the left side, appeared in 1565. To call the structure *ductus Botalli* is an anachronism, as it was in fact well known to Galen." (C. Singer, *The Evolutuon of Anatomy*, New York, 1925.) With what skill and precision Harvey describes the fetal circulation!

of animals with lungs, while the lungs are not used, as in those animals themselves without lungs.

So it seems obviously true in the fetus that the heart by its beat transfers blood from the vena cava to the aorta by as open a passage as if in the adult, as I have said, the two ventricles were united by removing the septum. Since these ways for the passage of blood are so conspicuous in the majority of animals,—indeed in all at certain times,—we must examine another matter. Why may we not conclude that this passage is made through the substance of the lungs in warm-blooded adult animals as man? Nature made these ways in the embryo at a time when the lungs were not used, apparently because of the lack of a passage through them. Why is it better, for Nature always does what is best, to close completely to the passage of blood in adolescence those open ways which are used in the embryos of so many animals, without opening any others for this transfer of blood?

The situation is such that those who seek the ways in man by which blood reaches the pulmonary vein and left ventricle from the vena cava, will do best to proceed by animal experimentation.[2] Here the reason

---

[2] Most of Harvey's doctrine was developed from studies in comparative anatomy and physiology. He was acutely aware of the value of animal experimentation, which had already been specifically recommended by Vesalius (1514-1564) and Realdus Columbus (1516-1559). There is evidence that Harvey deplored the suffering involved in animal experimentation, and that he spoke feelingly on it. (S. Weir Mitchell, *Some Recently Discovered Letters of William Harvey*, Phila.,

may be found why Nature, in larger adult animals, filters the blood through the lungs instead of choosing a direct path. No other way seems possible. It may be the larger, more perfect animals are warmer and when full grown their greater heat is thus more easily damped. For this reason the blood may go through the lungs, to be cooled by the inspired air and saved from boiling and extinction.³ There may be other reasons. To discuss and argue these points would be to speculate on the function of the lungs. I have made many observations on this matter, on ventilation, and on the necessity and use of air, as well as on the various organs in animals concerned in these matters. Nevertheless I shall leave these things to be more conveniently discussed in a separate tract lest I seem to wander too far from the proposition of the motion and function of the heart, and to confuse the question. Returning to our present concern, I shall go on with my demonstration.

1912, p. 50.) He may have used opium preparations to give analgesia, but there is no evidence favoring this view. It is not likely that he performed many experiments on higher animals, except such as were caught wounded in the King's hunts. R. Hannah has painted such a scene, where Harvey is demonstrating to Charles the heart of a deer slain in the chase.

³ The innate heat was supposed to reside in the blood, and the older theories on the heart beat and movement of the blood included the idea that the blood boiled up in the heart, and "boiled over" into the vessels, thus causing the heart beat and pulse. The function of respiration was thus to cool the heart. It is peculiar that Harvey should have permitted himself to utter this speculation when he so sarcastically attacked the current ideas on respiration and the cooling of the blood in the introduction.

In the more perfect warm-blooded adult animals, as man, the blood passes from the right ventricle of the heart through the pulmonary artery to the lungs, from there through the pulmonary vein into the left auricle, and then into the left ventricle. First I shall show how this may be so, and then that it is so.

CHAPTER VII

The Passage of Blood Through the Substance of the Lungs from the Right Ventricle of the Heart to the Pulmonary Vein and Left Ventricle

THAT this may be so, and that there is nothing to keep it from being so, is evident when we consider how water filtering through the earth forms springs and rivers, or when we speculate on how sweat goes through the skin, or urine through the kidneys. It is well known that those who use Spa waters, or those of *La Madonna* near Padua, or other acid waters which are drunk by the gallon, pass them all off in an hour or so by the bladder. So much fluid must tarry a while in the digestive tract, it must pass through the liver (everyone agrees that the alimentary succus goes through this organ at least twice daily),[1] through the veins, the substance of the kidneys, and through the ureters into the bladder.

I know there are those who deny that the whole mass of blood may pass through the lungs as the alimentary juices filter through the liver, saying it is

---

[1] I can't trace the origin of this quaint notion. Perhaps it refers to the two chief meals of the day.

impossible and unbelievable. They are of that class of men, as I reply with the poet, who promptly agree or disagree, according to their whim, fearful when wanted, bold when there is no need. The substance of the liver and also of the kidney is very dense, but that of the lung is much looser, and in comparison with the liver and kidney is spongy.[2] There is no propulsive force in the liver, but in the lung the blood is pushed along by the beat of the right ventricle of the heart, which must distend the vessels and pores of the lung. Again, as Galen indicates (*De Usu Part.*, *cap. 10*), the continual rising and falling of the lungs in respiration must open and close the vessels and porosities, as in a sponge or thing of similar structure when it is compressed and allowed to expand.[3] The liver, however, is quiet, it never seems to expand or contract.

---

[2] This later developed into the question of an "open" or a "closed" circulation through an organ. The microscopic structure of the internal organs, which gives the clue to their architecture and functional mechanism, was first investigated by Marcello Malpighi (1628–1694), the brilliant Italian scientist. In his *De pulmonibus* (1661) he gave the first clear conception of the structure of the lung, and completed Harvey's demonstration (announced the year of his birth) by proving the capillary anastomoses between arteries and veins. In his *De Viscerum structura* (1666) he outlined the structure of the liver, spleen, and kidney. The best modern work on the architecture of the kidney has been done by J. Henle (1809–1885), of the liver by F. P. Mall (1862–1917), and of the lung by W. S. Miller (1858–1939). The question of an open versus a closed circulation through an organ seems to be settled in favor of the latter.

[3] Respiration greatly influences both arterial and veinous pressures. It is generally agreed that blood-pressure rises during inspiration and falls during expiration. For a discussion of the factors involved, see

No one denies that all the ingested nourishment may pass through the liver to the vena cava in man and all large animals. If nutrition is to proceed, nutriment must reach the veins, and there appears to be no other way. Why not hold the same reasoning for the passage of blood through the lungs of adults, and believe it to be true, with Columbus, that great anatomist, from the size and structure of the pulmonary vessels, and because the pulmonary vein and corresponding ventricle are always filled with blood, which must come from the veins and by no other route except through the lungs? He and I consider it evident from dissections and other reasons given previously.

Those who will agree to nothing unless supported by authority, may learn that this truth may be confirmed by the words of Galen himself, that not only may blood be transmitted from the pulmonary artery to the pulmonary vein, then into the left ventricle, and from there to the arteries, but that this is accomplished by the continual beat of the heart and the motion of the lungs in breathing.

There are three sigmoid or semilunar valves at the opening of the pulmonary artery, which prevent blood forced into this pulmonary artery from flowing back into the heart. Galen clearly explains the functions of these valves in these words (*De Usu Part.*, *Lib. 6, cap. 10*): "*There is generally a mutual anastomo-*

W. H. Howell's *Physiology*, Phila., 1940, 14th Ed., p. 662–669, and K. J. Franklin's *A Monograph on Veins*, Springfield, Ill., 1937, p. 236–267.

sis or joining of the arteries and veins, and they transfer blood and spirit equally from each other by invisible and very small passages. If the mouth of the pulmonary artery always stayed open and Nature had no way of closing it when necessary or of opening it again, the blood could not transfuse through these invisible and delicate pores in the arteries during the contraction of the thorax. All things are not equally attracted or expelled. Something light is more easily drawn in by the distention of the part, and pushed out in contraction than something heavy. Likewise anything is more quickly passed through a wide tube than through a narrow one. When the thorax contracts, the pulmonary veins, strongly compressed on all sides, quickly expel some of the spirits in them, and take some blood from these tiny mouths. This could never happen if blood could flow back into the heart through the large opening of the pulmonary artery. Thus, its return through this great hole being blocked, and being compressed on every side, some of it filters into the arteries through these small pores."

Shortly after, in the next chapter: *"The more powerfully the thorax contracts, squeezing the blood, the more tightly do these membranes, the sigmoid valves, close the opening, so that nothing flows back."* A little before in the 10th chapter: *"Unless the valves be present, much difficulty would follow. The blood would follow this long course in vain, flowing in during the distention of the lungs and filling all the vessels in it, outwards during the constrictions, and tide-like, as Euripus, flow back and forth in a way not suited to the*

[64]

blood. This may not seem of much importance. Respiratory function, however, would suffer, and this would be of no little significance." Again, a little later: *"Another serious inconvenience would follow if our Maker had not provided these valves, the blood would move backwards during expirations."* So, in the 11th chapter, he concludes: *"It seems that all these valves have a common function in preventing regurgitation, appropriate to both directions, one set leading away from the heart and preventing return by that route, the other leading into the heart and preventing escape from it. Nature never wished to fatigue the heart with useless work, neither bringing anything unnecessarily to it, nor taking anything unnecessarily from it. Thus there are four openings, two in each ventricle, one of which leads into the heart, the other out of it."* A bit farther on: *"One of the blood-vessels fastened on the heart has a simple tunic, the other leading from it has a double tunic.* (Galen is referring to the right ventricle, but the same things apply to the left.) *The same cavity being provided for both of these, blood enters through the former and leaves through the latter."*

Galen proposes this argument to explain the passage of blood from the vena cava through the right ventricle to the lungs. By merely changing the terms, we may apply it more properly to the transfer of blood from the veins through the heart to the arteries. From the words of that great Prince of Physicians, Galen, it seems clear that blood filters through the lung from the pulmonary artery to the pulmonary vein as a result of the heart beat and the movement of the lungs and thorax. (Consult Hofmann's excellent Commentary on Galen's 6th Book, *De Usu Part.*, which I saw after writing this.)[4] The heart, further, continually receives blood in its ventricles, as into a cistern, and expels it. For this reason, it has four kinds of valves, two regulating inflow, and two outflow, so blood will not be inconveniently shifted back and forth like Euripus, neither flowing back into the part from which it should come, nor quitting that to which it should pass, lest the heart be wearied by vain labor and respiration be impeded. Finally, our assertion is clearly apparent, that the blood continually flows from the right to the left ventricle, from the vena cava to the aorta, through the porosities of the lung.

Since blood is constantly sent from the right ventricle into the lungs through the pulmonary

[4] Caspar Hofmann (1572-1648) was Professor of Medicine at Altdorf, and well recognized as one of the leading authorities on Galen. The book to which Harvey refers, *Comment. in Galen. de usu part.*, was published at Frankfort in 1625 (H. Haeser, *Geschichte der Medicin*, Jena, 1881, Vol. 2, p. 264). In 1636, Lord Arundel took his friend Harvey with him on a diplomatic mission to Vienna regarding a peace during the Thirty Years' War. Harvey wrote to Hofmann, offering in a very manly way to demonstrate his doctrines, which he had heard Hofmann opposed. See R. Willis' translation for the Sydenham Society, 1847, p. 595. "Tradition says that Harvey actually gave this demonstration in public, and that it proved satisfactory to everyone except Hofmann himself. The old man—then past the grand climacteric—remained unconvinced, and as he continued to urge objections, Harvey at length threw down his knife and walked out of the theatre" (D'Arcy Power's *William Harvey*. Lond., 1897, p. 114).

artery, and likewise constantly is drawn into the left ventricle from the lungs, as is obvious from what has been said and the position of the valves, it cannot do otherwise than flow through continuously. Then, as blood constantly pours into the right ventricle of the heart, and constantly moves out of the left, it is impossible, for the same reasons as above, obviously reasonable, for it to do otherwise than pass continually from the vena cava to the aorta.

It is evident from dissection that this occurs through wide open channels in all animals before birth, and from Galen's words and what has been said previously it is equally manifest that it occurs in adults by tiny pores and vascular openings through the lungs.[5] So it appears that, whereas one ventricle

---

[5] It is interesting to note how much Harvey relies on the traditional authorities to prove his points. The only contemporary authority referred to is R. Columbus (1516–1559), although M. Servetus (1509–1553), and A. Caesalpinus (1524–1603) had also described the pulmonary circulation. The latter, indeed, had discussed the general circulation, so naming the phenomenon, and had postulated *vasa in capillamenta resoluta,* or anastomoses between arteries and veins. Dr. J. C. Hemmeter (Johns Hopkins Hosp. Bull., 16: 165, 1905) suggests, in his excellent essay, that since both Servetus and Caesalpinus had offended the theologians, Harvey was afraid to mention them. It has been observed (Chap. IV, Note 6) that Harvey apparently had little fear of theological consequences. In view of Harvey's honesty it is hard to believe that he really knew of the work of these men. The "vascular openings" between arteries and veins were first demonstrated in the frog's lung by Marcello Malpighi (1628–1694), first great histologist: *De Pulmonibus Observationes Anatomicae,* Bologna, 1661, English translation by J. Young, Proc. Roy. Soc. Med., 23 (Sect. Hist. Med.) 1, 1929.

of the heart, the left, suffices for distributing blood to the body, and drawing it from the vena cava, as is the case in all animals lacking lungs, Nature was compelled, when she wished to filter blood through the lungs, to add the right ventricle, whose beat should force blood from the vena cava through the lungs into the left ventricle. Thus the right ventricle may be said to be made for the sake of transmitting blood through the lungs, not for nourishing them. It is entirely unreasonable to assume that the lungs need so much more abundant nutriment, and coming directly from the heart, so much purer and more spiritous blood than either the very refined substance of the brain, or the very brilliant and perfect structure of the eyes, or the flesh of the heart itself which is adequately nourished by the coronary artery.

Chapter VIII

Amount of Blood Passing Through the Heart from the Veins to the Arteries, and the Circular Motion of the Blood

SO FAR we have considered the transfer of blood from the veins to the arteries, and the ways by which it is transmitted and distributed by the heart beat. There may be some who will agree with me on these points because of the authority of Galen or Columbus or the reasons of others. What remains to be said on the quantity and source of this transferred blood, is, even if carefully reflected upon, so strange and undreamed of, that not only do I fear danger to myself from the malice of a few, but I dread lest I have all men as enemies, so much does habit or doctrine once absorbed, driving deeply its roots, become second nature, and so much does reverence for antiquity influence all men. But now the die is cast; my hope is in the love of truth and in the integrity of intelligence.

First I seriously considered in many investigations how much blood might be lost from cutting the arteries in animal experiments. Then I reflected on the symmetry and size of the vessels entering and leaving the ventricles of the heart, for

Nature, making nothing in vain, would not have given these vessels such relative greatness uselessly. Then I thought of the arrangement and structure of the valves and the rest of the heart. On these and other such matters I pondered often and deeply. For a long time I turned over in my mind such questions as, how much blood is transmitted, and how short a time does its passage take. Not deeming it possible for the digested food mass to furnish such an abundance of blood, without totally draining the veins or rupturing the arteries, unless it somehow got back to the veins from the arteries and returned to the right ventricle of the heart, I began to think there was a sort of motion as in a circle.

This I afterwards found true, that blood is pushed by the beat of the left ventricle and distributed through the arteries to the whole body, and back through the veins to the vena cava, and then returned to the right auricle, just as it is sent to the lungs through the pulmonary artery from the right ventricle and returned from the lungs through the pulmonary vein to the left ventricle, as previously described.

This motion may be called circular in the way that Aristotle says air and rain follow the circular motion of the stars.[1] The moist earth warmed by

---

[1] In spite of his own extraordinary discoveries, Harvey was remarkably conservative. N. Copernicus (1473–1543), J. Kepler (1571–1630), and G. Galilei (1564–1642) had overthrown the Ptolemical theory of the circular motion of the stars in the heavenly spheres, but Harvey seems never to have heard of their studies.

the sun gives off vapors, which, rising, are condensed to fall again moistening the earth. By this means things grow. So also tempests and meteors originate by a circular approach and recession of the sun.

Thus it happens in the body by the movement of the blood, all parts are fed and warmed by the more perfect, more spiritous, hotter, and, I might say, more nutritive blood. But in these parts this blood is cooled, thickened, and loses its power, so that it returns to its source, the heart, the inner temple of the body, to recover its virtue.

Here it regains its natural heat and fluidity, its power and vitality, and filled with spirits, is distributed again. All this depends on the motion and beat of the heart.

So the heart is the center of life, the sun of the Microcosm, as the sun itself might be called the heart of the world. The blood is moved, invigorated, and kept from decaying by the power and pulse of the heart. It is that intimate shrine whose function is the nourishing and warming of the whole body, the basis and source of all life. But of these matters we may speculate more appropriately in considering the final causes of this motion.

The vessels for the conduction of blood are of two sorts, the vena cava type and the aortic type. These are to be classified, not on the basis of structure or make-up, as commonly thought with Aristotle, for in many animals, as I have said, the veins do not differ from the arteries in thickness of tunics, but on the basis of difference in function or use. Both veins and arteries were called veins by the ancients, and not unjustly, as Galen notes. The arteries are the vessels carrying blood from the heart to the body, the veins returning blood from the body to the heart, the one the way from the heart, the other toward the heart,[2] the latter carrying imperfect blood unfit for nourishment, the former perfected, nutritious blood.

---

[2] In so clearly differentiating the functions of arteries and veins, why didn't Harvey go on and point out the confusion resulting from the terminology in use at the time with regard to the pulmonary vessels?

CHAPTER IX

The Circulation of the Blood is Proved by a Prime Consideration

IF ANYONE says these are empty words, broad assertions without basis, or innovations without just cause, there are three points coming for proof, from which I believe the truth will necessarily follow, and be clearly evident.

First, blood is constantly being transmitted from the vena cava to the arteries by the heart beat in such amounts that it cannot be furnished by the food consumed, and in such a way that the total quantity must pass through the heart in a short time.

Second, blood is forced by the pulse in the arteries continually and steadily to every part of the body in a much greater amount than is needed for nutrition or than the whole mass of food could supply.

And likewise third, the veins continually return this blood from every part of the body to the heart.

These proved, I think it will be clear that the blood circulates, passing away from the heart to the extremities and then returning back to the heart, thus moving in a circle.

Let us consider, arbitrarily or by experiment, that the left ventricle of the heart when filled in diastole, contains two or three ounces, or only an ounce and a half. In a cadaver I have found it holding more than three ounces. Likewise let us consider how much less the ventricle contains when the heart contracts or how much blood it forces into the aorta with each contraction, for, during systole, everyone will admit something is always forced out, as shown in Chapter III, and apparent from the structure of the valves. As a reasonable conjecture suppose a fourth, fifth, sixth, or even an eighth part is passed into the arteries. Then we may suppose in man that a single heart beat would force out either a half ounce, three drams, or even one dram of blood, which because of the valvular block could not flow back that way into the heart.

The heart makes more than a thousand beats in a half hour, in some two, three, or even four thousand. Multiplying by the drams, there will be in half an hour either 3,000 drams, 2,000 drams, five hundred ounces, or some other such proportionate amount of blood forced into the arteries by the heart, but always a greater quantity than is present in the whole body. Likewise in a sheep or dog, suppose one scruple goes out with each stroke of the heart, then in half an hour 1,000 scruples or about three and a half pounds of blood[1] would be

---

[1] The apothecaries or troy weight is used: 3 scruples equal 1 dram; 8 drams equal 1 ounce; 12 ounces equal 1 pound. This was in general use in Europe. This chapter is the crucial point in Harvey's

pumped out. But as I have determined in the sheep, the whole body does not contain more than four pounds of blood.

On this assumption of the passage of blood, made as a basis for argument, and from the estimation of the pulse rate, it is apparent that the entire quantity of blood passes from the veins to the arteries through the heart, and likewise through the lungs.

But suppose this would not occur in half an hour, but rather in an hour, or even in a day, it is still clear that more blood continually flows through the heart than can be supplied by the digested food or be held in the veins at any one time.

It cannot be said that the heart in contracting sometimes pumps and sometimes doesn't, or that it propels a mere nothing or something imaginary. This point has been settled previously, and besides, it is contrary to common sense. If the ventricles must be filled with blood in cardiac dilatation, something must always be pushed out in contraction, and not a little amount either, since the passages are not small nor the contractions few. This quantity expelled is some proportion of the contents of the ventricle, a third, a sixth, or an eighth, and an equivalent amount of blood must fill it up in diastole, so that there is a relation between the ventricular

---

argument, and the first instance of the quantitative method in physiology. It introduced the most important method of reasoning in the science and demonstrated its most significant truth.

capacity in contraction and in dilatation. Since the ventricles in dilating do not become filled with nothing, or with something imaginary, so in contracting they never expel nothing or something imaginary, but always blood in an amount proportionate to the contraction.

So it may be inferred that if the heart in a single beat in man, sheep, or ox, pumps one dram, and there are 1,000 beats in half an hour, the total amount pumped in that time would be ten pounds five ounces; if two drams at a single stroke, then twenty pounds ten ounces; if half an ounce, then forty-one pounds eight ounces; and if one ounce, then a total of eighty-three pounds four ounces, all of which would be transferred from the veins to the arteries in half an hour.

The amount pumped at a single beat, and the factors involved in increasing or diminishing it, may perhaps be more carefully studied later from many observations of mine.[2]

---

[2] Harvey says nothing more about this most important proposition, and his "observations," probably on animals, have been lost. The subject is of great current interest and is reviewed in Y. Henderson's *Volume Changes of the Heart*, Physiol. Rev., 3: 165, 1923, in C. H. Best and N. B. Taylor's *Physiological Basis of Medical Practice*, 2nd Ed., Balt., 1939, p. 367-378, and in J. Plesch's *Physiology and Pathology of Heart and Blood Vessels*, Oxford, 1937, p. 25-50. Discussions of experimental methods and findings are given in R. Tigerstedt's *Physiologie des Kreislaufes*, 2nd Ed., Berlin, 1921, Vol. 1, pp. 179-208, and by B. Kisch, *Handbuch der Normalen und Pathologischen Physiologie*, Berlin, 1927, Vol. 7 (2nd part) (*Blutzirkulation*), 1161-1204. For estimating cardiac output in man four methods have been proposed: 1. roentgenographic comparison of cardiac volume at systole and diastole (W. Meek and J. Eyster, Amer. J. Roentgenol., 7: 471, 1920;

Meanwhile I know and state to all that the blood is transmitted sometimes in a larger amount, other times in a smaller, and that the blood circulates sometimes rapidly, sometimes slowly, according to temperament, age, external or internal causes, normal or abnormal factors, sleep, rest, food, exercise, mental condition, and such like.[3]

Amer. J. Physiol., 63: 400, 1923; P. Hodges and J. Eyster, Amer. J. Roentgenol., 12: 252, 1924); 2. an application of the Fick principle (A. Fick, Sitz.-ber. d. phys.-med. Ges. Wurzburg, 1: 16, 1870), involving an indirect determination of the oxygen or carbon-dioxide tensions in mixed venous blood (S. Burwell and G. Robinson, J. Clin. Invest., 1: 47, 1924; H. Field, A. Bock, *et al.*, *ibid.*, 1: 65, 1924); 3. measuring the rate with which either a normally present gas (nitrogen, A. Bornstein, Arch. f. d. ges. Physiol., 132: 307, 1910), or a foreign gas is exchanged during the passage of the blood through the lungs (nitrousoxide, A. Krogh and J. Lindhard, Skand. Arch. f. Physiol., 27: 100, 1912; ethyl iodide, Y. Henderson and H. Haggard, Amer. J. Physiol., 73: 193, 1925; ethylene, E. Marshall and A. Grollman, *ibid.*, 86: 117, 1928; acetylene, A. Grollman, *ibid.*, 88: 432, 1929; 93: 116, 1930), and 4. an application of Stewart's principle (G. Stewart, J. Physiol., 22: 159, 1897) of the intravenous injection of an easily detectable foreign substance and the calculation of cardiac output from its concentration in arterial blo~ ˡɔ (W. Hamilton, J. ᴹᵒore, *et al.*, Amer. J. Physiol., 84: 338, 1928; 89: 322 and 331, 1929). Of fundamental importance is Grollman's observation that the basal cardiac output of normal humans is, like basal oxygen consumption, a function of body surface area and hence quite accurately predictable (Amer. J. Physiol., 90: 210, 1929). Under standard conditions it is 2.2 ± 0.3 liters of blood per square meter per minute, with an average deviation from the mean of 5 per cent. Contrary to the common view a compensatory mechanism exists in man which maintains a relatively constant cardiac output despite postural changes (Amer. J. Physiol., 86: 285, 1928). A total variation of less than 10 per cent was found during very frequent observations on two individuals for one year (Amer. J. Physiol., 93: 536, 1930).
[3] This amazing statement by Harvey, based on we know not what evidence, has been quantitiatively confirmed by A. Grollman (*The Cardiac Output of Man in Health and Disease*, Springfield, Ill., 1932).

But suppose even the smallest amount of blood be transmitted through the lungs and heart at a single beat, a greater quantity would eventually be pumped into the arteries and the body than could be furnished by the food consumed,[4] unless by constantly making a circuit and returning.

The matter is obvious in animal experimentation. If an opening be cut not only in the aorta, but even in a small artery, as Galen claims, in man, the whole blood content may be drained from the entire body, from veins as well as arteries, in almost half an hour's time.

Butchers can also well enough confirm this point. In killing an ox by cutting the arteries of the neck, the whole mass of blood may be drained off and all the vessels emptied in less than a quarter of an

---

"The ingestion of large amounts of fluid causes a moderate rise in the cardiac output which is greater after the ingestion of isotonic saline than after the ingestion of water. The splanchnic dilatation which follows the ingestion of food is accompanied by a large increase in the cardiac output for several ꞌᴴᵁ᙮ ⁻ Psychic disturbance ᷆ᴣ᷉e found to cause an elevation in the cardiac output." Grollman's work should be carefully read.

⁴ This was the crux of the argument to Harvey, since the Galenists insisted that blood was formed in the liver ("natural spirits") from the food consumed, and distributed by the veins to nourish the parts of the body according to their needs. Hence the emphasis placed by Harvey in proving, by most conservative estimates, that the heart pumps in a relatively short time more blood than is needed for nutrition or than food can supply, more in fact than the whole weight of the man or animal. Obviously it must be the same blood going around and around. The introduction of quantitative evidence into physiological problems was Harvey's great philosophical contribution, and he apparently realized it, for he uses it again and again with telling effect.

hour. We know how quickly an excessive hemorrhage may occur in removing a tumor or in an amputation.

The force of this argument would not be lost by saying that blood flows equally if not more from veins than from arteries, in butchering or amputating. The contrary of this really holds. Because they collapse, and have no power to propel blood, and because there is a block where the valves are placed, as shall be shown later, the veins really pour out little blood. The arteries, however, squirt it out in quantities, with force, as if ejected from a syringe. The matter may be tested by cutting the artery in the neck of a sheep or dog, but leaving the vein alone, and it will easily be seen with how much force, in what amounts, and how quickly all the blood in the body is drained, from veins as well as arteries. The arteries receive blood from the veins in no other way than by transmission through the heart, as previously said. So by ligating the aorta close to the heart, there need be no uncertainty about finding the arteries empty if they be opened in the neck or elsewhere, and the veins filled.

The reason is now apparent why so much blood is found in the veins in anatomical dissection, and so little in the arteries, so much in the right side of the heart, so little in the left. This fact probably led the ancients to believe that arteries contained only spirits during an animal's life. The reason for the difference is probably as follows.[5] There is no other passage from the veins to the arteries except through the heart and lungs, so when an animal expires and the lungs stop moving, the blood is prevented from passing from the pulmonary artery to the pulmonary vein and then into the left ventricle of the heart. This is like what was noted previously in the embryo, where the transit is prevented by the lack of motion in the lungs and the opening and closing of its tiny pores. The heart, however, does not stop at the same time as the lungs, but outlives them and continues to beat. The left ventricle and the arteries continue to send blood to the rest of the body and into the veins, but, receiving none from the lungs, they soon become empty.

This fact awakens not a little belief in our position, since it can be ascribed to no other reason than what we have proposed.

It further appears that the greater or more vehemently the arteries pulsate, the quicker will the body be exhausted of its blood in a hemorrhage. Hence in fainting or alarm, when the heartbeats

---

[5] One reason has already been given. Is this an interpolation or addition to the original draft? There is much evidence that the book was not composed as a whole, but that it is a combination of many scattered notes written at different times. Respiration is quite a factor in maintaining circulation. Dr. R. M. Waters, well-known anesthetist, has told me of several instances where artificial respiration has maintained a circulation when the heart has failed.

slowly and feebly, a hemorrhage is reduced or stopped.

This is also why one cannot draw forth by any effort more than half the blood by cutting the jugular or femoral veins or arteries in a dead body after the heart stops beating. Nor may a butcher succeed in bleeding an ox after hitting it on the head and stunning it, if he does not cut its throat before the heart stops beating.

Finally, it may now be suspected why no one so far has said anything to the point on the place, manner, or purpose of the anastomosis of veins and arteries. I shall now discuss this point.[6]

---

[6] But he doesn't. This point is quite forgotten. Further evidence of assembling the treatise from notes written at different times. The subject of capillary physiology is well reviewed in original extracts in J. F. Fulton's *Selected Readings in the History of Physiology*, Springfield, Ill., 1930, pp. 61-105.

CHAPTER X

*The First Proposition, Concerning the Amount
of Blood Passing from Veins to Arteries,
During the Circulation of the Blood,
is Freed from Objections, and
Confirmed by Experiments*

WHETHER the matter be referred to calculation or to experiment and dissection,
the important proposition has been established that
blood is continually poured into the arteries in a
greater amount than can be supplied by the food.
Since it all flows past in so short a time, it must be
made to flow in a circle.

Someone may say here that a great amount may
flow out without any necessity for a circulation
and that it all may come from the food. An example might be given in the rich milk supply of the
mammae. A cow may give three or four, or even
seven and more gallons of milk daily, and a mother
two or three pints when nursing a baby or twins,
all of which must obviously come from the food.
It may be replied that the heart, by computation,
does more in an hour or less.

Not yet persuaded, one may still insist that cutting an artery opens a very abnormal passage through

which blood may forcibly pour, but that nothing like this happens in the intact body, with no outlet made. With the arteries filled, in their natural state, so large an amount cannot pass in so short a time as to make a return necessary. It may be replied that from the computation and reasons already given, the excess contained in the dilated heart in comparison with the constricted must be in general pumped out with each beat and this amount must be transmitted, as long as the body is intact and in a natural state.

In serpents and certain fishes by ligating the veins a little below the heart, you will see the space between the ligature and the heart quickly become empty. So, unless you deny what you see, you must admit the blood returns to the heart. This will be clear later in discussing the second proposition.

We may close here with a single conclusive example, by which anyone may be convinced by his own eyes.

If a live snake be cut open, the heart may be seen quietly and distinctly beating for more than an hour, moving like a worm and propelling blood when it contracts longitudinally, for it is oblong. It becomes pale in systole, the reverse in diastole, and almost all the other things we have mentioned as proving the truth may be clearly observed, for here all happens slower and more distinctly. This especially may be seen more clearly than the midday sun. The vena cava enters at the lower part of the heart, the artery leaves at the upper. Now, pinching off the vena cava with a forceps or between finger and thumb, the course of blood being intercepted some distance below the heart, you will see that the space between the finger and the heart is drained at once, the blood being emptied by the heart beat. At the same time, the heart becomes much paler even in distention, smaller from lack of blood, and beats more slowly, so that it seems to be dying. Immediately on releasing the vein, the color and size of the heart returns to normal.[1]

On the other hand, leaving the vein alone, if you ligate or compress the artery a little distance above the heart, you will see the space between the compression and the heart, and the latter also, become greatly distended and very turgid, of a purple or livid color, and, choked by the blood, it will seem to suffocate. On removing the block, the normal color, size, and pulse returns.

This is evidence of two kinds of death, failure from a lack, and suffocation from excess. In these examples of both, one may find proof before his eyes of the truth spoken about the heart.

---

[1] These experiments have been beautifully reproduced in moving-pictures under the skillful direction of Sir Thomas Lewis and Professor H. H. Dale of London (*The Harvey Film*).

CHAPTER XI

The Second Proposition is Proven

OUR second proposition may appear more clearly by considering certain experiments from which it is obvious that blood enters a limb through the arteries and returns through the veins, that the arteries are the vessels carrying blood from the heart and the veins the channels returning it to the heart, and that, in the extremities, blood passes from arteries to veins directly by anastomosis or indirectly through pores in the flesh, as discussed before in regard to its transfer from veins to arteries in the heart and thorax. From this it may be clear that it moves in a circle from the center to the extremities and back from the extremities to the center.

Then, making certain calculations, it will also be clear that the quantity may neither be supplied from the food taken in nor necessarily be required for nutrition.

These experiments will also clear up some points regarding ligatures: why they may cause swelling, which is neither by heat nor suction nor any reason yet known; what uses and advantages may be obtained from them in practice; how they may either suppress or provoke hemorrhage; how they may cause gangrene in the limbs, and what their function may be in castrating animals or removing fleshy tumors.

Because no one has understood the rationale of these matters, it has happened that almost everyone recommends ligatures in treating disease on the authority of the ancients, and very few use them properly or get any benefit from them.

Some ligatures are tight, others middling. I call a ligature tight when it is pulled so firmly about a limb that the beat of the artery cannot be felt beyond it. We use this kind in amputations to control bleeding. This kind is also used in castrating animals and removing tumors, where we see the testicles and tumors dying and dropping off because the ligature keeps out heat and nourishment.

I call a ligature middling which compresses a limb on all sides, but without pain, so that the artery may still pulsate somewhat beyond the ligature. This type is used for "drawing," in bloodletting. The proper ligature for phlebotomy is applied above the elbow in such a manner that the artery at the wrist may still be felt beating slightly.

Now, let an experiment be made on a man's arm, using a bandage as in blood-letting, or grasping tightly with the hand.[1] The best subject is one

---

[1] These interesting experiments, discussed in a quantitative way in Chapter XIII, imply some of the factors involved in arterial and venous blood pressure. Attention was sharply drawn to the mechanical relations of blood-pressure by the Rev. Stephen Hales (1677-1761) and

who is lean, with large veins, warm after exercise when more blood is going to the extremities and the pulse is stronger, for then all will be more apparent. Under these conditions, place on a ligature as tightly as the subject can stand. Then it may be observed that the artery does not pulsate beyond the bandage, in the wrist or elsewhere. Next, just above the ligature the artery is higher in diastole and beats more strongly, swelling near the ligature as if trying to break through and flood past the barrier. The artery at this place seems abnormally full. The hand, however, retains its natural color and appearance. In a little time it begins to cool a bit, but nothing is "drawn" into it.

After this bandage has been on for some time, loosen it to the medium tightness used, as I said, in blood-letting. You will see the whole hand at once become suffused and distended, and its veins become swollen and varicosed. After ten or fifteen

---

experimental measurements reported in his *Statistical Essays: Haæmodynamics*, 1733. A valuable account of Hales has been given by P. M. Dawson (Johns Hopkins Hosp. Bull., 15: 185, 232, 1904). Further advance was made by J.-L.-M. Poiseuille (1799–1869), whose haemodynamometer was introduced in 1828, and whose studies on capillary flow appeared in 1840 (Compt. rend. Acad. sc., 11: 961.1041). In 1847 Carl Ludwig (1816–1895) invented the graphic method of recording blood-pressure, and thus greatly facilitated all phases of physiological analysis (Müller's Arch. Anat. Physiol., 1847, p. 242). A method for determining venous pressure in man was devised by J. A. E. Eyster and D. Hooker (Johns Hopkins Hosp. Bull., 19: 274, 1908). For a general disussion, see W. H. Howells' *Physiology*, 14th Ed., Phila., 1940, p. 477. Also Journ. Am. Med. Asso., 91: 31 (July 7) 1928.

beats of the artery you will see the hand become impacted and gorged with a great amount of blood "drawn" by this medium tight ligature, but without pain, heat, horror of a vacuum or any other cause so far proposed.

If one will place a finger on the artery as it beats at the edge of the bandage, the blood may be felt to flow under it at the moment of loosening. The subject, also, on whose arm the experiment is made, clearly feels, as the ligature is slackened, warmth and blood pulsing through, as though an obstacle has been removed. And he is conscious of it following the artery and diffusing through the hand, as it warms and swells.

In the case of the tight bandage, the artery is distended and pulsates above it, not below; in the mediumly tight one, however, the veins become turgid and the arteries shrink below the ligature, never above it. Indeed, in this case, unless you compress these swollen veins very strongly, you will scarcely be able to force any blood above the ligature or cause the veins there to be filled.

From these facts any careful observer may easily understand that blood enters a limb through the arteries. A tight bandage about them "draws" nothing, the hand keeps its color, nothing flows into it, neither is it distended. With a little slackening, as in a mediumly tight ligature, it is clear that the blood is instantly and strongly forced in, and the hand made to swell. When they pulsate, blood flows through them into the hand, as when a medium bandage is used, but otherwise not, with a tight ligature, except above it. Meanwhile, the veins being compressed, nothing can flow through them. This is indicated by the fact that they are much more swollen below the bandage than above it, or than is usual with it removed, and that while compressed they carry nothing under the ligature to the parts above. So it is clear that the bandage prevents the return of blood through the veins to the parts above it and keeps those below it engorged.

The arteries, however, for the simple reason that they are not blocked by the moderate ligature, carry blood beyond it from the inside of the body by the power and impulse of the heart. This is the difference between a tight and medium bandage, the former not only blocks the flow of blood in the veins but also in the arteries, the latter does not impede the pulsating force from spreading beyond the ligature and carrying blood to the extremities of the body.

One may reason as follows. Below a medium bandage we see the veins become swollen and gorged and the hand filled with blood. This must be caused by blood passing under the ligature either in veins, arteries or tiny pores. It cannot come through the veins, certainly not through invisible ducts, so it must flow through the arteries, according to what has been said. It obviously cannot flow through the veins since the blood cannot be squeezed back above the ligature unless it is completely loosened. Then we see the veins suddenly collapse, discharging themselves to the part above, the hand loses its flush, and the stagnant blood and swelling quickly fade away.

Further, he whose arm has been bound for some time with a medium bandage, and whose hand has been rendered somewhat swollen and cold, feels, as the ligature is loosened, something cold creeping up with the returning blood to the elbow or armpit. I think this cold blood returning to the heart, after removing the bandage in blood-letting, is a cause of fainting, which we sometimes see even in robust persons, usually when the ligature is removed, or, as is commonly said, when the blood turns.

Moreover, immediately on loosening a tight bandage to a medium one, we see the veins below it, but not the arteries, swollen with blood continually carried in by the arteries. This indicates that blood passes from arteries to veins, not the reverse, and that there is either an anastomosis of these vessels or pores in the flesh and solid parts permeable to blood. It also indicates that the veins inter-communicate, since, with a medium ligature above the elbow, they all swell up at the same time, and, if even a single venule be cut with a lancet, they all quickly shrink, giving up their blood to this one, and subside almost together.

Anyone may understood from this the reasons for the "drawing" power existing in ligatures, and perhaps in all fluxes. It is clear how the blood cannot escape from the hand when the veins are compressed with what I call a medium bandage, but being driven in by the heart beat through the arteries, and not being able to escape anywhere, the part must necessarily become gorged and swollen.

How can it be otherwise? Heat, pain, and the suction of a vacuum have a certain "drawing" power to fill a part, but not to distend or swell it abnormally, nor to overcome it so suddenly and powerfully by impact of blood that the flesh and vessels are in danger of being torn or ruptured. It is neither believable nor demonstrable that heat, pain, or the *vis vacui* can do this.

Furthermore, this "drawing" power occurs in a ligature without pain, heat, or the suction of a vacuum. If pain happens to "draw" any blood, with the arm tied above the elbow, how may the hand and fingers and their veins become swollen below the ligature, since because of its pressure, blood cannot get there through the veins? And why is neither swelling, nor sign of venous filling or engorgement, nor any vestige of "drawing" apparent above the ligature?

The obvious cause of the "drawing" or abnormal swelling in the hand and fingers below the bandage is the forceful and copious influx of blood which cannot escape. Indeed, is not the cause of all tumors and oppressive swellings, what Avicenna says, that the way in is open but the way out closed, so there must be an engorgement or tumor?

May not this happen in boils? As long as the swelling is increasing and has not come to a final state, a full pulse may be felt in the area, especially in more acute tumors in which the swelling is sudden. But these are for later investigation. However, this happened in an accident I experienced. I was thrown once from a carriage and struck my head at a place where an arterial branch crosses the temporal region. Immediately I felt, in the space of about twenty pulsations, a tumor the size of an egg but without either heat or great pain. It seems the blood was pushed out with an unusual amount and speed because of the nearness of the artery to the place of injury.

Now it also appears why, in phlebotomy, if we wish the blood to flow longer and with greater force, we ligate above the cut, not below. If such a flow would come through the veins above, the ligature would not only be of no aid, but would positively hinder it, for if blood flowed downwards from the upper part of an extremity through the veins, it would more properly be tied below the cut so the impeded blood would escape through the cut more abundantly. But since it is forced elsewhere through arteries into the veins lower down, from which return is prevented by the ligature, the veins swell, and being under tension can eject their contents through the opening to some distance with unusual force. When the bandage is loosened, and the returning channels opened, the flow sinks to not more than a drop at a time. Everyone knows in performing phlebotomy that if you either loosen the bandage, tie below the cut, or bind the limb too tightly, the blood will escape without force, because in the latter the influx of blood through the arteries is blocked by the tightness of the ligature, while in the former the venous return is not properly checked because of its looseness.

CHAPTER XII

That There is a Circulation of the Blood Follows from the Proof of the Second Proposition

SINCE these things are so, it establishes the proof of what I said previously, that blood continually passes through the heart. For we have seen that blood spreads from the arteries to the veins, not from veins to arteries; we have seen further that almost the total amount of blood can be taken from an arm if a single cutaneous vein be opened with a lancet and a bandage properly applied, and we have seen still further, that there is so much force behind it, and so sufficient a flow that the blood may easily and quickly be withdrawn not only in the amount present in the arm below the ligature before the cut was made, but in the whole arm, and in the entire body, arteries as well as veins.

So it must be admitted, first, that blood is supplied with force and impetus to push it beneath the ligature, for it escapes with vigor, which is derived from the pumping action of the heart and from this alone. Likewise, it must be further admitted that this flow comes from the heart, and by way of the heart, by a transfer accomplished from the great veins, since it passes through the arteries beneath the ligature, not through veins, and arteries never receive blood from veins except by way of the left ventricle of the heart. Nor could any such an amount be drawn from a single vein anywhere, a bandage being applied above it, especially with such force, such an amount, or so easily and quickly, except by the beating power of the heart in the manner described.

If these things are so, we may very readily compute the amount of blood and come to some conclusion on its circular motion. If, for instance, in phlebotomy, one were to let the blood flow with its usual force and rate for a half hour, there is no doubt but that the greater part of it would be drained off, practically emptying not only arteries but also the great veins, and that fainting and syncope would follow. It is reasonable to assume that as great an amount of blood as is lost in this half hour's time, passed from the great veins through the heart to the aorta. Further, if you figure how many ounces of blood flow through a single arm, or pass under a medium bandage in twenty or thirty heart-beats, you will have a basis for estimating how much flows through the other arm in the same time, or through both sides of the neck, or through both legs, and through all the other arteries and veins of the body. Since all these are continually supplied with fresh blood, which must flow through the lungs and ventricles of the heart, from the veins, it must be accomplished in a circuit, since the amount involved is much more than can be furnished from the food consumed, or than is needed for the nourishment of the parts.

It is further to be observed that this truth is often demonstrated in blood-letting. Though you properly bandage the arm, and puncture the vein correctly with a lancet, if a fainting state of mind comes on through fear or any other cause, and the heart beats more sluggishly, blood will escape only a drop at a time, especially if the ligature be made a little more tight. The reason is that the feeble beat in the compressed artery, with the weaker propelling power, cannot force the blood under the bandage.[1] For the same reason the feeble and languid heart cannot force the normal amount of blood through the lungs or transfer it from the veins to the arteries. In the same way and for the same reasons, it happens that the menses of women and all types of hemorrhages are checked. If the opposite occurs, the patient recovering his mind, and losing his fear, you will see the arteries at once beat more powerfully, even in the bound-off part, so the blood gushes from the opening and flows steadily.

---

[1] A characteristic example of Harvey's clear reasoning. It is easily inferred that the obvious factor in maintaining blood pressure is the pumping action of the heart.

Chapter XIII

The Third Proposition is Proven, and the Circulation of the Blood is Demonstrated from it

SO FAR we have considered the amount of blood flowing through the heart and lungs in the body cavity, and similarly from the arteries to the veins in the periphery. It remains for us to discuss how blood from the extremities gets back to the heart through the veins, and whether or not these are the only vessels serving this purpose. This done we may consider the three basic propositions proving the circulation of the blood so well established, so plain and obvious, as to force belief.

This proposition will be perfectly clear from a consideration of the valves found in the venous cavities, from their functions, and from experiments demonstrable with them.

The celebrated anatomist, Hieronymus Fabricius of Aquapendente, or, instead of him, Jacobus Sylvius, as Doctor Riolan wishes it, first described membranous valves in the veins, of sigmoid or semilunar shape,[1] and being very delicate eminences

---

[1] Hieronymus Fabricius of Aquapendente (1537–1619) was a pupil of G. Fallopius (1523–1562) who was in turn the pupil of Vesalius (1514–1564). It was their establishment of modern anatomy

on the inner lining of these vessels. They are placed differently in different individuals, but are attached to the sides of the veins, and they are directed upwards toward the main venous trunks. As there are usually two together, they face and touch each other, and their edges are so apt to join or close that they prevent anything from passing from the main trunks or larger veins to the smaller branches. They are so arranged that the horns of one set are opposite the hollow part of the preceding set, and so on alternately.

The discoverer of these valves and his followers did not rightly appreciate their function. It is not to prevent blood from falling by its weight into areas lower down, for there are some in the jugular vein which are directed downwards, and which prevent blood from being carried upwards. They are thus not always looking upwards, but more correctly, always towards the main venous trunks and the

which gave such glory to Padua where they taught. Harvey studied under Fabricius from 1598 to 1602. Vesalius was a pupil of J. Sylvius (1478–1555) at Paris.

It is likely that G. Canano (1515–1578) first described the valves in the veins. C. Estienne (d. 1564) had observed valves in the portal veins (not present in man) in 1538, and J. Sylvius commented on them posthumously. The first published drawings of venous valves were by S. Alberti, *De Valvulis*, 1585, who acknowledged indebtedness to Fabricius. The latter demonstrated them publicly in 1579 and published his *De venarum osteolis* in 1603. Harvey employed to make his two plates the same Frankfort craftsman who had made the copper-plates for the 1624 edition of Fabricius (H. Cushing and E. C. Streeter, *Monumenta Medica, IV, Canano,* Florence, 1925). K. J. Franklin's careful translation of Fabricius' work (*De Venarum Osteolis (1603) of Hieronymus Fabricius of Aquapendante (1533?–1619)*, Springfield, Ill., 1933), contains a delightful biobibliographical account of Fabricius as well as a comprehensive historical survey of knowledge on the valves of the veins.

heart. Others as well as myself have sometimes found them in the milky veins[2] and in the venous branches of the mesentery directed towards the vena cava and portal vein. To this may be added that there are none in the arteries, and that one may note that dogs, oxen, and all such animals have valves at the branches of the crural veins at the top of the sacrum, and in branches from the haunches, in which no such weight effect of an erect stature is to be feared.

Nor, as some say, are the valves in the jugular veins to prevent apoplexy, since the head is more likely to be influenced by what flows into it through the carotid arteries.[3] Nor are they present to keep blood in the smaller branches, not permitting it to flow entirely into the larger more open trunks,

---

[2] Does Harvey mean the lacteals? The Galenical error, to which Harvey subscribed, that the veins of the mesentery carried chyle to the liver, was cleared up by G. Aselli (1581–1626) who discovered the lacteals (*De lactibus*, Milan, 1627), by J. Pecquet (1622–1674) who showed their passage to the thoracic duct and then to the subclavian vein (*Experimenta nova*, Paris, 1651), and by O. Rudbeck (1639–1702) and T. Bartholin (1616–1680) who discovered the intestinal lymphatics and their connection with the thoracic duct. Pecquet's work contained a carefully devised proof of Harvey's doctrine. On April 28, 1652, Harvey wrote a letter to Dr. R. Morison of Paris (see Willis's translation of Harvey's works, Sydenham Society, 1847, p. 604) in which he discussed Pecquet's contribution. His characteristic conservatism prevented him from accepting the discovery, although it offered a demonstrable explanation of an unsatisfactory portion of his own.

[3] An idea partially expressed in their very name, "the arteries of sleep." This name may have developed from the early observation (used for anesthetic purposes by the Assyrians) that pressure on these vessels might be followed by fainting. The physiological significance of the carotids has been superbly revealed by C. Heymans (*Le Sinus Carotidien*, Paris, 1933).

for they are placed where there are no branches at all, although I confess they are more frequently seen where there are branchings. Nor are they present for slowing the flow of blood from the center of the body, for it seems likely it would flow slowly enough anyway, as it would then be passed from larger to smaller branches, become separated from the source and mass, and be moved from warmer to cooler places.

The valves are present solely that blood may not move from the larger veins into the smaller ones lest it rupture or varicose them, and that it may not advance from the center of the body into the periphery through them, but rather from the extremities to the center. This latter movement is facilitated by these delicate valves, the contrary completely prevented. They are so situated that what may pass the horns of a set above is checked by those below, for whatever may slip past the edges of one set is caught on the convexity of those beyond, so it may not pass farther.

I have often noticed in dissecting veins, that no matter how much care I take, it is impossible to pass a probe from the main venous trunks very far into the smaller branches on account of the valvular obstructions. On the contrary it is very easy to push it in the opposite direction, from the branches toward the larger trunks. In many places a pair of valves are so placed that when raised they join in the middle of the vein, and their edges are so nicely united that one cannot perceive any crack along their junction. On the other hand, they yield to a probe introduced from without inwards and are easily released in the manner of flood-gates opposing a river flow. So they intercept, and when tightly closed, completely prevent in many places a flow of blood back from the heart and vena cava. They are so constituted that they can never permit blood to move in the veins from the heart upwards to the head, downwards toward the feet, or sidewise to the arms. They oppose any movement of blood from the larger veins toward the smaller ones, but they favor and facilitate a free and open route starting from the small veins and ending in the larger ones.

This fact may be more clearly shown by tying off an arm of a subject as if for blood-letting (*A, A,* fig. 1). There will appear at intervals (especially in rustics) knots, or swellings, like nodules (*B, C, D, E, F*), not only where there is branching (*E, F*), but also where none occurs (*C, D*). These are caused by the valves, appearing thus on the surface of the hand and arm. If you will clear the blood away from a nodule or valve by pressing a thumb or finger below it (*H,* fig. 2), you will see that nothing can flow back, being entirely prevented by the valve, and that the part of the vein between the swelling and the finger (*H, O,* fig. 2), disappears, while above the swelling or valve it is well distended (*O, G*). Keeping the vein thus empty of blood, if you will press downwards against the valve, (*O*, fig. 3) by a finger of the other hand on the distended upper portion (*K*, fig. 3), you will note that nothing can be forced through the valve. The greater effort you make the more the vein is distended toward the valve, but you will observe that it stays empty below it (*H*, *O*, fig. 3).

From many such experiments it is evident that the function of the valves in the veins is the same as that of the three sigmoid valves placed at the opening of the aorta and pulmonary artery, to prevent, when they are tightly closed, the reflux of blood passing over them.

Further, with the arm bound as before and the veins swollen, if you will press on a vein a little below a swelling or valve (*L*, fig. 4) and then squeeze the blood upwards beyond the valve (*N*) with another finger (*M*), you will see that this part of the vein stays empty, and that no back flow can occur through the valve (as in *H*, *O*, fig. 2). But as soon as the finger (*H*) is removed, the vein is filled from below (as in *D*, *C*, fig. 1). Thus it is clearly evident that blood moves through the veins toward the heart, from the periphery inwards, and not in the opposite direction. The valves in some places, either because they do not completely close, or because they occur singly, do not seem adequate to block a flow of blood from the center, but the majority certainly do. At any rate, wherever they seem poorly made, they appear to be compensated

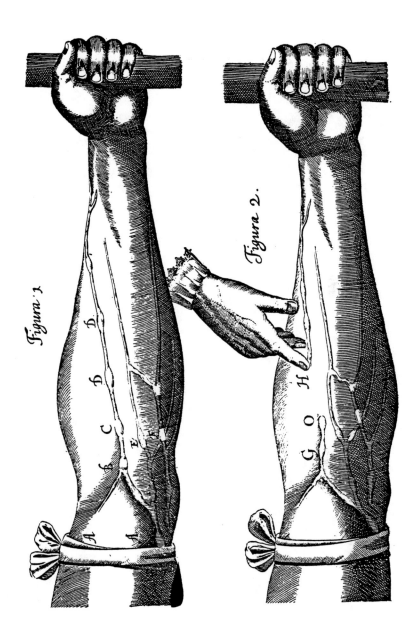

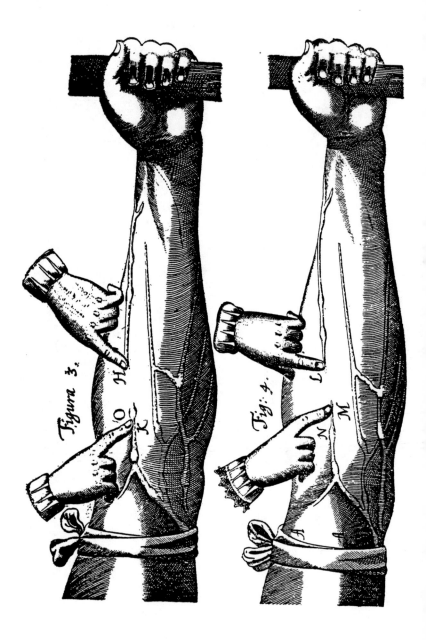

for in some way, by the greater frequency or better action of the succeeding valves. So, as the veins are the wide open passages for returning blood to the heart, they are adequately prevented from distributing it from the heart.

Above all, note this. With the arm of your subject bound, the veins distended, and the nodes or valves prominent, apply your thumb to a vein a little below a valve so as to stop the blood coming up from the hand, and then with your finger press the blood from that part of the vein up past the valve (*L*, *N*, fig. 4), as was said before. Remove your thumb (*L*), and the vein at once fills up from below (as in *D*, *C*, fig. 1). Again compress with your thumb, and squeeze the blood out in the same way as before (*L*, *N*, and *H*, *O*), and do this a thousand times as quickly as possible. By careful reckoning, of course, the quantity of blood forced up beyond the valve by a single compression may be estimated, and this multiplied by a thousand gives so much blood transmitted in this way through a single portion of the veins in a relatively short time, that without doubt you will be very easily convinced by the quickness of its passage of the circulation of the blood.

But you may say this experiment of mine violates natural conditions. Then if you will take as long a distance from the valve as possible, observing how quickly, on releasing your thumb, the blood wells up and fills the vein from below, I do not doubt but that you will be thoroughly convinced.

Chapter XIV

Conclusion of the Demonstration of the Circulation of the Blood

BRIEFLY let me now sum up and propose generally my idea of the circulation of the blood.

It has been shown by reason and experiment that blood by the beat of the ventricles flows through the lungs and heart and is pumped to the whole body. There it passes through pores in the flesh into the veins through which it returns from the periphery everywhere to the center, from the smaller veins into the larger ones, finally coming to the vena cava and right auricle. This occurs in such an amount, with such an outflow through the arteries, and such a reflux through the veins, that it cannot be supplied by the food consumed. It is also much more than is needed for nutrition. It must therefore be concluded that the blood in the animal body moves around in a circle continuously, and that the action or function of the heart is to accomplish this by pumping. This is the only reason for the motion and beat of the heart.

Chapter XV

The Circulation of the Blood is Confirmed by Plausible Methods

IT WILL not be irrelevant here to point out further that even according to common ideas, the circulation is both convenient and necessary. In the first place, since death is a dissolution resulting from lack of heat, all living things being warm, all dying things cold (*Aristotle, De Respir., lib. 2 & 3, De Part. Animal.,* etc.), there must be a place of origin for this heat. On this hearth, as it were, the original native fire, the warming power of nature, is preserved. From this heat and life may flow everywhere in the body, nourishment may come from it, and on it all vegetative energy may depend.

That the heart is this place and source of life, in the manner just described, I hope no one will deny.

The blood, then, must move, and in such a way that it is brought back to the heart, for otherwise it would become thick and immobile, as Aristotle says (*De Part. Animal., lib. 2*), in the periphery of the body, far from its source. We note that motion always generates and preserves heat and spirit, while in quietness they disappear. So the blood, in the extremities, thickens from the cold and loses its spirit, as in death. Thus it must come back to its source and origin to take up heat or spirit or whatever else it needs to be refreshened. We often see the extremities so chilled by a cold atmosphere that the hands, nose, and cheeks seem deathly blue. The blood in them, stagnating as in the lower parts of a corpse, become livid. The limbs are sluggish and are moved with difficulty, so that they seem almost deprived of life. In no other way can they recover heat, color, and life so completely and especially so quickly as by a freshly driven flow of heat from the source. But how can they, when heat and life are almost gone, draw anything into them? How can they, filled with congealed stagnant blood, admit fresh blood and nourishment, unless they give up their old contents? Thus the heart really is the center where this exhausted blood recovers life and heat, as Aristotle says (*De Respirat.*, *lib. 2*). New blood imbued with heat and spirit by it and sent out through the arteries, forces onwards the chilled and stagnant stuff, and the failing warmth and vitality is restored in all parts of the body.

Hence as long as the heart is uninjured, life and health can be restored to the body generally, but if it is exhausted or harmed by any severe affliction, the whole body must suffer and be injured.[1] When-

---

[1] This sentence is the one clear note in a chapter badly fogged by speculations based on the traditional natural philosophy. Note the rather weak illustration from a field in which the footing is still

ever the source is damaged, nothing, as Aristotle says (*De Part. Animal., lib. 3*), can help it or anything depending on it. Perhaps, by the way, this is the reason why anguish, love, jealousy, worry, and similar mental states are accompanied by emaciation, wasting away, and other bodily changes predisposing to disease and consumption in men. A mental disturbance provoking pain, excessive joy, hope or anxiety extends to the heart, where it affects its temper,[2] and rate, impairing general nutrition and vigor. It is no wonder many serious diseases thus gain access to the body, when it is suffering from faulty nourishment and lack of normal warmth.

Further, since all animals live by food digested internally, the distribution of this concoction must be achieved, and hence there must be a place where the aliment is perfected and from which it is apportioned the to separate members. This place is the heart. It is the only organ containing blood

---

very uncertain. Harvey was apparently quite interested in the mind body problem as may also be noted in his *De generatione*, 1651. How was it that he failed to pick up valvular lesions of the heart in his many autopsies? Certainly to so keen an observer the effects of an insufficient or stenotic valve would have been obvious, in the light of his discovery. Mitral stenosis and aortic insufficiency were apparently first described in detail by R. Vieussens (*Traité nouveau de la structure et des causes de mouvement natural de coeur*, Toulouse, 1715).

[2] The ancient Greeks commented upon the obvious effects of strong emotion on cardiac action. This may have been one reason why Empedocles and Aristotle made the heart the abiding place of thought. Even the ancient Jewish scribe wrote that "every imagination of the *thoughts of his heart* was only evil" (Genesis 6:5).

for general use, referring not to that specifically used in the coronary arteries and veins, but to the general reserve in the cavities of its auricles and ventricles, since all the others have a blood supply for their own particular use. The heart alone is so situated and constructed as a reservoir and fountain that blood may be apportioned from it and distributed by its beat to all regions according to the size of the artery serving them.

Moreover, force and effort, such as given by the heart, is needed to distribute and move the blood this way. Blood easily concentrates toward the interior, as drops of water spilled on a table tend to run together, from such slight causes as cold, fear, or horror. It also tends to move from the tiny veins to the intermediate branches and then to the larger veins because of the movements of the extremities and the compression of muscles. So it is more inclined to move from the periphery toward the interior, even though valves offered no opposition to the contrary. Therefore, blood requires force and impulse to be moved from its origin against its inclination into more narrow and cooler channels. Only the heart can furnish this, and in the manner already described.

CHAPTER XVI

The Circulation of the Blood is Supported by its Implications

—•——◆>●<◆——•—

ASSUMING the truth of this proposition there are certain consequences which are useful in coaxing belief *a posteriori*. Although some of them may seem to be clouded in considerable doubt, a reasonable case may easily be made for them.

How does it happen that in contagious conditions like poisoned wounds, bites of serpents or mad dogs, or lues, the whole body may become diseased while the place of contact is often unharmed or healed? Lues commonly appears at first with pain in the shoulders and head, or by other symptoms, the genitals meanwhile being uninjured. We know that the wound made by a mad dog may have healed when fever and the rest of the unpleasant symptoms supervene. Without doubt it happens that the contagion, first being deposited in a certain spot, is carried by the returning blood to the heart, from which later it is spread to the whole body.[1]

---

[1] The usual drainage from the tissues is now considered to be through the lympathics. These pass through nodules of lymphoid tissue in which "the contagion,"—bacteria or other foreign bodies,—

In tertian fever, the cause of the sickness first seeking the heart, lingers about the heart and lungs and causes shortness of breath, sighing and languor. This happens because the vital energy is depressed, and because the blood, driven into the lungs, thickens and cannot pass through, as I have noted in autopsies on those dying during the beginning of the disease. Then the pulse is rapid, feeble, and somewhat irregular. When the heat increases, the blood thins out, and an open passage is made, then the whole body warms, the pulse becomes strong and full during the febrile state, while the abnormal heat kindled in the heart is scattered from there to the body, through the arteries, along with the morbific matter, which is thus naturally dissolved and overpowered.[2]

This may also explain why some medical agents applied to the skin have almost as much effect as if taken by mouth. Colocynth and aloes applied externally move the bowels, cantharides excites

---

may be filtered out before the lymph passes into the veins. Harvey's reasoning here gave a new turn to the old humoral pathology, again unfortunately neglected by physicians until long after.

[2] It is interesting, in view of our present conceptions of immune reactions to infectious processes, that Harvey should have implied that fever is a beneficial response in the infected individual. The success of Peruvian or Jesuits' bark,—called cinchona from the Spanish Countess Chinchona, one of the first Europeans to benefit from it (1638),—in relieving malarial fevers, obscured the significance of Harvey's implication until recently. The general feeling developed that the fever should be reduced at any cost. Hence the extraordinary interest with the rise of synthetic organic chemistry in the "antipyretics."

the urine, garlic placed on the feet promotes expectoration, cordials invigorate, and so on.[3] It is not unreasonable to say that the veins take up through their openings some of the things applied externally and carry them in with the blood, not unlike the way in which those in the mesentery absorb chyle from the intestines, and carry it along with blood to the liver.

Blood enters the mesentery through the coeliac, and the superior and inferior mesenteric arteries, and passes to the intestines. From these, along with chyle drawn in by the veins, it is returned by their many ramifications to the portal vein and the liver, and from this to the vena cava.[4] The blood in these veins is the same color and consistency as in other veins, contrary to general opinion.

It is not true that there are two opposite movements in these capillaries, chyle inward and blood outward. To be so must be considered incongruous and improbable rather than constituted by the great wisdom of Nature. If chyle were mixed with blood, the raw with the concocted, in equal parts, no coction, or blood formation would follow. Rather there would be a mixture of the two as in the mingling of wine in water or syrup. But when a very small amount of chyle is added to a lot of blood,

---

[3] The factors concerned in skin absorption have attracted much attention since the development of chemical warfare. No studies have been made, that I know of, on the materials mentioned here.

[4] See Note 2, Chapter XIII.

it is more comparable, as Aristotle says, to adding . a single drop of water to a cask of wine, or the reverse. Then the total is not a mixture, but remains either wine or water. So in dissecting the mesenteric veins, chyme and blood are not found either separately or mixed, but only the same blood in color and consistency as appears in the other veins. Still, since there is some chyle or unconcocted material, however small, in this, Nature has interposed the liver, in whose winding passages it delays and undergoes more change, lest coming too quickly in the rough to the heart, it suppress vitality.

Hence there is almost no use for the liver in the embryo. The umbilical vein clearly passes right through the liver, with an opening or anastomosis to the portal vein, so that fetal blood returning from the intestines does not flow through the liver, but mixed with maternal blood from the placenta goes to the heart through this umbilical vein. So in the development of the fetus, the liver is among the last parts formed. In the human fetus we often see all the organs fully marked out, even the genitals, while there is still almost no trace of the liver. At the time when all the organs, even the heart, appear white, and there is no sign of redness anywhere except in the veins, you will see nothing where the liver should be except an irregular spot like blood spilled out of a ruptured vein.

In the developing egg there are two umbilical veins, one passing through the liver directly to the heart from the white of the egg, the other from the yolk ending in the portal vein. The chick is developed and nourished first by the white, then after it is formed and leaves the shell, from the yolk. One may find the yolk in the stomach of a chick many days after hatching, for it serves instead of the milk in other animals.

These matters, however, may be more appropriate to notes on the formation of the fetus, where many problems of the following sort can be discussed. Why is one part formed first, another later? Concerning the origin of organs, whether one may be a cause of another, and much about the heart. Why, as Aristotle points out (*De Part. Animal, Lib. 3*), is it the first to take shape, and seem to have life, motion, and sensation before any other part of the body? Likewise, why does blood appear before anything else, and how does it possess the vital animal principle? How does it desire to be moved here and there, for which reason the heart seems to be provided?

In the same way, speculating on the pulse, why does one kind indicate death, another recovery? In considering all varieties of pulse, what do they signify and why? Likewise, in discussing crises, natural discharges, nutrition, the distribution of nutriment, and fluxes.

Finally, in considering all phases of medicine, physiology, pathology, and therapeutics, I realize how many problems may be answered, how many doubts removed, and how much obscurity cleared up by the truth and light here given.[5] It opens up a field so vast that were I to scan it further or investigate it more fully this little effort would swell to a huge volume which perhaps would take more than my ability or span of life to finish.

In the following chapter, therefore, reference will only be made to the functions and causes derived from an anatomical study of the heart and arteries. Even here I shall find much which may be explained by my theory, and which in turn will make it more clear. Above all, I wish to confirm and illustrate it by anatomical reasoning.

There is one point, however, which might be noted here, although it belongs more properly in my discussion of the function of the spleen.[6] From

---

[5] Did Harvey mean this treatise to be a "preliminary communication?" It seems doubtful that there would be much to add to what is here written or to what may be inferred from it. Harvey probably was honest in the remark here made,—he realized what still could be done but was willing to let others take up the burden, while he himself was anxious to let it drop.

[6] This paragraph seems to have been another after-thought. If Harvey ever wrote a discussion of the function of the spleen, it was apparently lost with his other papers during the plunderings of the Civil War. If this note is an example of the many observations Harvey felt could be made in the light of his doctrine, it would better have been omitted. A typical Galenical argument, straining to find the "design" in nature, this is the antithesis of most of the clear-cut observations and explanations in this book. The majority of these are directly in the modern spirit of simple description with an attempted explanation of the mechanism involved. Harvey was in fact among the first to emphasize the *how* in physiology, rather than the more conceited and arrogant *why*. For a discussion of the functions of the spleen including Barcroft's work see E. B. Krumbhaar, Physiol. Rev., 6:160, 1926.

the upper part of the splenic branch leading to the pancreas arise the posterior coronary, gastric, and gastroepiploic veins, all of which are spread in many branches on the stomach, like the mesenterics on the intestines. Likewise, into the lower part of this splenic vessel empty the hemorrhoidal veins from the colon and rectum. Through both these venous systems returning blood is poured into the splenic branch, carrying with it from the stomach a crude watery juice not completely chylified, and from the feces a thick earthy material. Both these are appropriately tempered by natural mixture, although difficultly concocted alone, because of opposite defects. Then, diluted by a large amount of warm blood flowing through the spleen from its large artery, the mixture enters the portal of the liver in a better state of preparation. The defects of either extreme are made up and compensated by this arrangement of the veins.

CHAPTER XVII

The Motion and Circulation of the Blood is Established by What is Displayed in the Heart and Elsewhere by Anatomical Investigation

-··──────➤·❂·◄────────···

I DO not find the heart a separate and distinct organ in all animals. Some, called plant-animals, have no heart at all. These animals are colder, have little bulk, are softer, and of uniform structure, such as grubs, worms, and many which come from decayed material and do not preserve their species.[1] These need no heart to impel nourishment to their extremities, for their bodies are uniform and they have no separate members. By the contraction and relaxation of the whole body they take up and move, expel and remove aliment. Oysters, mussels, sponges

---

[1] Harvey really says "*generated* from decayed material." This idea of spontaneous generation, current from the beginning of philosophical speculation, received its first serious blow from Francesco Redi (1626–1694) in his *Experientia circa generationem insectorum*, Amsterdam, 1671. Another attack, covering microscopic forms of life, was given by L. Pasteur (1822–1895). In his *De generatione animalium*, (London, 1861), Harvey maintained the theory that the organism is not preformed in the ovum, but that it gradually evolves by growth and union of its parts. This, as Garrison says, "subverted the ancient concept that life is engendered out of corruption (or putrefaction)." A. W. Meyer has recently prepared a thorough analysis of Harvey's *De Generatione* (Stanford, 1936). The question of spontaneous generation has arisen again in connection with filterable viruses.

and the whole genus of zoophytes or plant-animals have no heart, for the whole body functions as a heart, and the animal itself is a heart.

In almost the entire family of insects we cannot clearly discern a heart because of the smallness of the body. In bees, flies, hornets, and the like, one can see with a magnifying glass something pulsate. Likewise in lice, in which, since they are translucent, you can easily watch, with a magnifying glass[2] for enlarging, the passage of food like a black spot through the intestines.

In bloodless and colder animals as snails, shrimps, and shell-fish there is a pulsating place like a vesicle or auricle without a heart. This may be seen beating and contracting, slowly indeed, and only in the summer or warmer seasons.

In these this part is fashioned because there is need for some impulse to distribute nutriment on account of the variety of separate organs or the denseness of their substance. But the beats are seldom and sometimes entirely fail through cold. This is appropriate to their doubtful nature as they sometimes seem living, sometimes dying, sometimes showing the vitality of animals, sometimes of

---

[2] In the miserable little Longhine edition, Bologna, 1697, with the Archbishop's *imprimatur*, the word *microscopia* is inserted. I was using this edition for translating, and was greatly puzzled that Harvey should have employed such a term. When I received the facsimile of the original edition, my difficulties were not over, but just beginning, for I then had to check over my whole translation, to avoid any other such errors!

plants. This seems also to occur in insects which hide away in winter and appear dead or show a vegetative vitality. But that it happens in red-blooded animals[3] as frogs, turtles, or serpents may justly be doubted.

In larger, warmer, red-blooded animals there is need for something with greater power to distribute nourishment. So, to fishes, serpents, lizards, turtles, frogs and such like, a heart is granted with both an auricle and ventricle. Thus it is very true, as Aristotle contended (*De Part. Animal., Lib. 3*), that no red-blooded animal lacks a heart, by whose beat the nourishing liquid is not only stirred up more vigorously than by an auricle, but is propelled farther and more quickly.

In still bigger, warmer, and more perfect animals with more fervent and spiritous blood, a more robust and fleshy heart is needed to pump the nutritive fluid with greater force and speed, on account of the size and density of their bodies. Further, because the more perfect animals need more perfect nourishment and more native heat, that the aliment may be better concocted[4] and delivered,

---

[3] Harvey just says "blooded animals." The oxygen carrying pigment in invertebrates is not the iron containing hemoglobin but a copper containing hemocyanin, which is not red colored.

[4] It is interesting to watch the valiant groping towards the facts regarding the oxygenation of blood in the lungs. The idea expressed is that in order better to "perfect" blood from the food, more heat is needed for the process in the liver, and, as was generally recognized, a draft of air promoted burning and heating. But the traditional doctrines, which Harvey follows in his teleological speculations

it is convenient for these animals to have lungs and another ventricle to send nouishment through these lungs.

Wherever there are lungs there are two ventricles in the heart, a right and left, and wherever there is a right there is also a left, but not the reverse. I call that the left ventricle which is distinguished by function, not position, the one namely that sends blood to the whole body, not merely to the lungs. This left ventricle seems to comprise the real heart. It is medianly placed, marked with deeper furrows, and made with greater care, so that the heart seems to have been formed for the sake of the left ventricle. The right ventricle is a sort of servant to the left, it does not reach to the apex, its walls are three-fold thinner, and it is somehow joined on to the left, as Aristotle says. Its capacity indeed is greater since it not only furnishes material to the left but also nourishment to the lungs.

It is noteworthy that this is otherwise in the embryo, where there is no such difference between the ventricles. As in the double kernels of a nut, they about equal each other, and the tip of the right reaches the apex of the left, so that the heart appears as a double-pointed cone. Here, as I have said, blood does not pass through the lungs from

---

through some of the chapters of this book, are full of the many contradictions against which he is so bitter in the Introduction. In the present instance, for example, it was also taught that respiration existed for cooling the heart, to keep the blood from boiling and extinction (Note 3, Chapter VI).

the right side of the heart to the left. Both ventricles equally have the same function of transferring
blood from the vena cava to the aorta through the
foramen ovale and the *ductus arteriosus*, and of
pumping it to the whole body, whence their structural equality.

However, when the lungs are used and it is time
for the passages spoken of to be closed, then these
differences in the ventricles begin to appear, since
the right pumps only through the lungs, but the
left through the whole body.

There are also so-called braces in the heart, many
fleshy and fibrous bands, which Aristotle calls
nerves (*De. Respirat. & De Part. Animal., Lib. 3*).
They are stretched partly from place to place, and
partly in the walls and septum, where they form
little pits. Little muscles are concealed in these
furrows which are added to assist in a more powerful contraction of the heart and a more vigorous
expulsion of blood.[5] Like the clever and elaborate
arrangement of ropes on a ship, they help the heart
to contract in every direction, driving blood more
fully and forcibly from the ventricles.

It may be shown, however, that some animals
have less than others, that in all animals with them,
they are more numerous and stronger in the left
than in the right ventricle, and in some animals where

---

[5] These *papillary muscles*, elongated into the *chordae tendinae* which
extend to the valves, seem to aid in closing the valves more exactly.
See Note 5, Chapter II.

they are present in the left, none are found in the right chamber. In man there are more in the left than in the right ventricle, and more in the ventricles than in the auricles, and in some subjects it seems there are none in the auricles. In large, muscular, peasant-type individuals there are many, in more slender frames, and in women, few.

In some animals the ventricles of the heart are smooth inside, entirely without fibers or bands. In almost all small birds, serpents, frogs, turtles, and such like, and in most all fishes, neither fibers, or so-called nerves, nor tricuspid valves are found in the ventricles.

In some animals the right ventricle is smooth inside while the left has these fibrous bands, as in the goose, swan, and heavier birds. The reason is the same here as elsewhere. Since the lungs are spongy, loose, and soft, not so great a force is needed to pump blood through them. Therefore the right ventricle either has none of these fibers or they are few and weak, not fleshy or muscular. Those of the left ventricle, however, are stronger, more numerous, and more muscular because this chamber needs to be more powerful since it must propel blood farther through the whole body. This is also why the left ventricle is placed in the middle of the heart, and has walls three times as thick and strong as the right.

So all animals, man included, that have a stronger and more sturdy frame, with large, brawny limbs some distance from the heart, have a more thick, powerful, and muscular heart, as is obvious and necessary. On the contrary, those whose structure is more slender and soft have a more flaccid, less massive, and weaker heart, with few or no fibers internally.

Consider likewise the function of the sigmoid valves. These are so made that blood once received into the ventricles of the heart, or sent into the pulmonary artery or aorta, can not regurgitate. When they are raised and tightly joined, they form a three pointed line, like the bite of a leech, and the more tightly they are forced shut, the more do they block the reflux of blood.

The tricuspids are like gate-keepers at the point of inflow from the vena cava and pulmonary vein, so that the blood, when strongly propelled, may not escape back into them. They are not present in all animals, for the reason stated, nor do they seem to have been made with the same efficiency in those in which they are found.[6] In some they are made

---

[6] This again raises the question as to whether or not Harvey ever noted insufficiency or stenosis of the valves in humans. He is speaking as an comparative anatomist here.

According to Galen (J. C. Dalton, *Doctrines of the Circulation*, Phila., 1884, p. 250), Erasistratus named the right auriculo-ventricular valves "tricuspids" (τριγλωχινας), and also called the valves at the openings of the pulmonary artery and aorta "sigmoid" in shape. Since the old Greek *sigma* had the form of the letter C, this gave a correct impression of their semilunar form. Vesalius, in his immortal *De Humani Corporis Fabrica*, Basle, 1543, p. 592, first likens the left auriculo-ventricular valves to a bishop's miter.

to fit exactly, in others poorly and negligently, so that they may be closed according to the greater or lesser impulse from the contraction of the ventricles. In the left ventricle, therefore, that the closure may be made more complete against the stronger impulse, there are only two, placed like a miter, and lengthened in a conical form so they may come together medianly and close very exactly. This probably led Aristotle to consider this ventricle double, divided transversely. Likewise, that blood may not escape back into the pulmonary vein and thus reduce the power of the left ventricle to pump blood through the whole body, these mitral valves surpass in size, strength, and exactness of closure those placed in the right ventricle. Hence, necessarily, no heart can be found without a ventricle since there must be a source and store-house for blood.

The same does not always hold for the brain.[7] Almost no kind of bird has a ventricle in the brain, as is clear in the goose and swan, whose brains nearly equal in size that of the rabbit. But the rabbit has ventricles in the brain while the goose does not.

Wherever there is a single ventricle in the heart, a flaccid, membranous, hollow, blood-filled auricle is appended. Where two ventricles exist, there are like-

---

[7] This paragraph and the last sentence of the preceding seem to be unnecessary appendages to the argument. They appear in the middle of a long paragraph which has been broken up for greater ease in reading. Was Harvey implying that there is no necessary store-house for "animal spirits" in the brain as there is for "vital-spirits" (or blood) in the heart?

wise two auricles. On the other hand, in some animals there is an auricle without a ventricle, or anyway a sac like an auricle, or the vein itself, dilated in one place, pulsates. This is seen in hornets, bees, and other insects, in experiments on which I think I can show not only a pulse but also a respiration in that part called a tail. This can be seen to lengthen and contract, sometimes quickly, sometimes slowly, as the insect seems to be blown up and to need more air. But more of this in the Treatise on Respiration.[8]

Likewise it is clear that the auricles beat, contract, and, as I said before, push blood into the ventricles. So wherever there is a ventricle, an auricle is needed. Not alone, as commonly believed, to be a receptacle and store-house for blood. For what use is a pulsation in retaining? The auricles exist as the initial motive power of the blood. Especially the right auricle, the first to live and the last to die, as said before. They are necessary in order to cast the blood conveniently into the ventricles. These, continually contracting, throw out more fully and forcibly the blood already in motion, just as a ball-player can send a ball harder and farther by striking it on a rebound than if he simply throws it. Moreover, contrary to common opinion, neither the heart nor anything else can draw anything into itself by dilating or distending, unless like a sponge previously compressed, while it is return-

---

[8] If the *Treatise on Respiration* was written, it was probably destroyed by the Parliamentary soldiers who sacked Harvey's rooms in Whitehall in 1642, when Harvey was with Charles I at Edgehill.

ing to its real condition.⁹ All local motion in an animal first takes place from the contraction of some particular part. Thus blood is cast into the ventricles by auricular contraction, as shown before, and then passed on and distributed by the ventricular contraction.

I have been interested in getting at the truth of this matter of local motion. How the initial motivating organ in all animals having a prime motive spirit is, as Aristotle says in his book *De Spiritu,* contractile; how νευρον is derived from νεϝω (*nuto, contraho*), and how Aristotle had more than a superficial acquaintance with muscles, and on that account referred all motion in animals to nerves and a contractile part, and hence called those bands in the heart nerves,—all this I hope to make clear soon, if I am permitted to demonstrate my observations on the organic motion of animals and the structure of muscles.¹⁰

---

⁹ According to present physiological conceptions, venous pressure is great enough to open the auriculo-ventricular valves during diastole, so that considerable blood flows into the ventricles while they are relaxed and before the auricles start to contract. It is generally agreed with Harvey that the ventricles have no suction power, but it is felt that the contractions of the auricles force in only a portion of the ventricular contents. See Note 4, Chapter IV.

¹⁰ This treatise also disappeared. The derivation of terms is apparently offered in apology for Aristotle's calling the muscular bands in the heart "nerves." G. A. Borelli (1608–1679), in developing a mechanical analysis of muscular motion carried over a theory of contraction caused by a liquid discharge from nerves (*De motu animalium*, 1680). For a helpful discussion of the physiology of muscle consult J. F. Fulton's monograph, Baltimore, 1927.

But to go on with our subject, on the function of the auricles in filling the ventricles with blood, it may be observed that the thicker and denser the walls of the heart itself, the more fibrous and muscular are the auricles, and the reverse. In some animals the auricle appears to be a bloody membranous sac, as in fishes, where it is so delicate and ample that it seems to float above the heart. In other fishes as the carp, and barbel, in which this vesicle is a little more fleshy, it bears a striking resemblance to lungs.

In some men of heavier and huskier build, the right auricle is so robust and so well braced inside by bands and various connecting fibers that it approximates in strength the ventricle of other subjects. I marvel that there is such variation in this in different men.

It is noteworthy that the auricles are disproportionately large in the fetus, because they are present before the rest of the heart is made or can take up its function, so that, as shown before, they assume the duty of the whole heart.

My observations previously referred to on the development of the fetus, and which Aristotle confirms in regard to the egg, throw great light on this matter. While the fetus is till soft like a worm, or, as is said, in the milk,[11] there is a single bloody spot, or pulsating sac, as if a part of the umbilical vein

---

[11] I can't trace the origin or significance of this expression. My wretched Longhine edition, Bologna, 1697, rendered *vermicules* as *ventricules*, and *lacte* as *lucte!*

were dilated at its base or origin. After awhile when the fetus is outlined and the body begins to be more substantial, this vesicle becomes more fleshy and stronger, and its constitution changing, it turns into the auricles. From these the bulk of the heart begins to sprout, although as yet it has no function. When the fetus is really developed, with bones separated from fresh, when the body is perfected and has motion, then the heart actually beats and, as I said, pumps blood by both ventricles from the vena cava to the arteries.

Thus divine Nature making nothing in vain, neither gives a heart to an animal where it is not needed, nor makes one before it can be used. By the same steps in the development of every animal, passing through the structural stages, I might say, of egg, worm, and fetus, it obtains perfection in each. These points are confirmed elsewhere by many observations on the formation of the fetus.[12]

Hippocrates, in the book *De Corde*, did not call the heart a muscle without good reason.[13] Its action or

[12] Another paragraph stressing the "Bridgewater treatise" idea. Harvey was probably engaged, while this was published, on his other great treatise, *De generatione animalium*, which appeared at the solicitation and under the direction of Dr. George Ent, in London in 1651. This is a remarkable volume, not yet properly annotated or appreciated, a mine of observation and interpretation, and a complete commentary on the ideas of Aristotle and Fabricius on fetal development. As a sustained intellectual effort it surpasses the present volume, and with the development of sexual physiology may be recognized as a very significant contribution.

[13] This little tract of about 800 words ($\pi\epsilon\rho\iota$ $\kappa\alpha\rho\delta\iota\eta s$) is the best anatomical work of the Hippocratic Collection, and is available in a

function is that of a muscle, to contract and to move something, namely its content of blood.

As in the muscles themselves, the actions and uses of the heart may be understood from the arrangement of its fibers and the structure of its movable parts. Anatomists generally agree with Galen that the heart is composed of a variety of fibers arranged straight, transversely, and obliquely. But in the boiled heart the fibers are seen to be arranged otherwise. All those in the walls and septum are circular as in a sphincter whereas those in the bands are longitudinally oblique.[14] So when all these muscles contract simultaneously the apex is pulled toward the base by the bands and the walls are drawn together in a sphere. The heart is contracted on all sides and the ventricles are compressed. Hence it must be recognized that since it acts by contraction, its function is to pump blood into the arteries.

------

recent English translation by F. R. Hurlbutt, Jr. (Bull. Hist. Med., 7: 1104, 1939). Written about 400 B. C., it describes the auriculo-ventricular and semilunar valves, and the *chordae tendinae.* Air is said to enter the heart and change the blood. The conception of the heart as a muscle is not usually credited either to Harvey or the Hippocratic writer. It is characteristic of Harvey to attempt to fortify his ideas by references to the classical authorities. See Note 3, Chapter II.

[14] Interesting that Harvey boiled the heart to get a clear picture of its fibrous make-up. The best recent analysis of this subject was made by F. P. Mall (Amer. J. Anat., 2: 211, 1911). Mall describes a deep and superficial "bulbospiral" and "sinospiral" system of fibers which curve around from the base to the apex of the heart. These form a sling-like support for the circular fibers which are especially thick on the left side. Harvey's description is essentially correct. See W. H. Howell's *Physiology*, 14th Ed., Phila., 1940.

No less should it be agreed with Aristotle in such questions on the significance of the heart as whether it receives motion and sensation from the brain, or blood from the liver, or whether it is the source of the veins and blood, and so on. Those who try to refute him here overlook or do not understand the significance of his argument. This is, that it is the first to exist, and contains in itself blood, vitality, sensation and motion before the brain or liver are formed, or can be clearly distinguished, or at least before they can assume any function. The heart is fashioned with appropriate structures for motion, as an internal organism, before the body. Being finished first, Nature wished the rest of the body to be made, nourished, preserved, and perfected by it, as its work and home. The heart is like the head of a state, holding supreme power, ruling everywhere.[15] So in the animal body power is entirely dependent on and derived from this source and foundation.

Many points about the arteries further illustrate and confirm this truth. Why doesn't the *arteria venosa* pulsate, since it is considered an artery? Why may a pulse be felt in the *vena arteriosa*?[16] Because

---

[15] This is the general Aristotelian position.

[16] The *arteria venosa* is the pulmonary vein, the *vena arteriosa* the pulmonary artery.

In the last sentence of this paragraph my Latin lexicon (E. A. Andrews, New York, 1852) permits me to translate *impetum* literally as pressure, but not *impellentis* as pumping! Harvey does not anywhere in the treatise use a word which may literally be translated to give the conception of the heart as a pump. Retaining the tradi-

the pulse in an artery is due to an impact of blood. Why do the arteries differ so much from veins in the thickness and strength of their walls? Because they must withstand the pressure of the pumping heart and rushing blood.

Hence, since Nature makes nothing in vain, and does the best everywhere, the nearer arteries are to the heart the more do they differ from veins in structure. Here they are stronger and more ligamentous,[17] but in their terminal branchings, as in the hands, feet, brain, mesentery, and testicles, they are so similar to veins in make up that it is hard to tell one from another by ocular examination of their tunics. This occurs from the following good reason: the farther an artery is away from the heart the less it is reached by the cardiac pressure dissipated by the long space. Since all the arterial trunks and branches must be filled with blood, the cardiac impulse is further diminished, divided in a way by each branching.

So the terminal arteries appear like veins, not only in structure, but also in function, for they rarely show a perceptible pulse unless the heart beats more violently, or the arteriole dilates or is more open at the particular point.[18] Thus it happens that we may

---

tional semi-technical language of the subject, he perhaps never thought of using a word which conveys the meaning he so clearly implies.

[17] This is the nearest Harvey comes to grasping the idea of the elasticity of blood-vessel walls, a factor of considerable importance in determining blood pressure.

[18] A remarkable explanation, implying vaso-constriction and

sometimes be aware of a pulsation in the teeth, fingers or inflammatory tumors, other times not. By this symptom I have diagnosed fever in children, whose pulse is naturally rapid anyway. By holding tightly the fingers of a young and delicate person I can easily perceive pulsation there when the fever is high.

On the other hand, when the heart beats more feebly, as in fainting, hysteria, asphyxia, and in the very weak and moribund, it is impossible to feel a pulse not merely in the fingers, but even at the wrist or temple.

Here, lest they be deceived, surgeons should be advised that when blood flows with force from a wound, in amputations, or in removing a fleshy tumor, it always comes from an artery. Not always in spurts, however, since the small arteries may not pulsate, especially if compressed by a bandage.

Further, here is the same reason why the *vena arteriosa* not only has the structure and walls of an artery but also why it does not differ so much from the veins in the thickness of its walls as the aorta. The latter sustains a greater impulse from the left ventricle, than the former from the right. The walls of the pulmonary artery are softer in structure than those of the aorta to the same extent as the walls and flesh of the right ventricle are weaker than those of

---

dilatation, another important factor in determining blood pressure. Harvey correctly notes vascular dilatation in local inflammatory reactions, and cutaneous vascular dilatations in fever.

the left. The lungs are relatively softer in texture than the flesh and bulk of the body in the same degree that the walls of the pulmonary artery differ from those of the aorta. This general proportion holds quite universally. The stronger, more muscular, and more substantial the build of men, the thicker, heavier, more powerful and fibrous the heart, and the auricles and arteries are proportionally increased in thickness, strength, and all other respects.

On the other hand, in fish, birds, serpents, and other such families of animals, the ventricles of the heart are smooth inside, without villi or valves. The walls are thinner and the arteries scarcely differ from the veins in thickness of tunics.

Further, why do the lungs have such large vessels, veins as well as arteries, for the trunk of the pulmonary veins exceeds both crurals and jugulars, and why are they filled with so much blood? We know by experience in autopsies and the advice of Aristotle, not to be deceived by the appearance of such animals as we encounter in dissection which have been bled to death. The reason is that the source and storehouse of the blood, and the place for its perfecting, is in the lungs and heart.

Similarly, why do we find the pulmonary vein and left ventricle in dissections so full of the same black clotted blood which fills the right ventricle and pulmonary artery? Because blood continually traverses the lungs from the right side of the heart to the left.

Finally, why has the so-called *vena arteriosa* the

structure of an artery, while the *arteria venosa* has that of a vein? Because really, in build, in function and everything, the former is an artery, the latter a vein, contrary to what is commonly believed.[19] Why has the pulmonary artery so large an opening? Because it carries much more blood than is needed for the nourishment of the lungs.

All these phenomena and many others noted in dissecting, if correctly judged, seem clearly to illustrate and to confirm the truth announced in this tract, and at the same time to refute popular opinion. Certainly it would be hard to explain in any other way why all these matters are so made and constituted except in a manner conforming to my theory and to what I have expounded.

---

[19] Since he so clearly points out the inconsistencies of the current names, why did not Harvey rename these vessels? One may sometimes be too deferential to traditional authority.

"LOOKING OVER THE SEA"

Harvey's Statue in His Birthplace, Folkstone, Looks Down on the Waters of Invasion.

—Photograph by Elizabeth Leake

"THE MOST PLEASING PICTURE OF DR. WILLIAM HARVEY"

Usually attributed to Sir Anthony Van Dyck (1599-1641), this dignified painting is in the possession of the heirs of Richard Bright (1789-1858), the celebrated physician to Guy's Hospital. Note the crest similar to the "stemma" to Harvey at Padua, and the motto, not found elsewhere.

—Courtesy of the Oxford University Press.

APPENDIX I

CHRONOLOGY OF THE LIFE OF WILLIAM HARVEY

Chronology *of* William Harvey

1578. Born (April 1) at Folkestone, Kent, of Thomas (a town official) and Joane Hawke Harvey, eldest of "a week of sons, whereof this William was bred to learning, his other brethren being bound apprentices in London, and all at last ended in effect in merchants." (Fuller).

1588. Excitement over and defeat of the Spanish Armada. How thrilled was Harvey entering Canterbury Grammar School this year?

1593. Entered Caius College, Cambridge, implying choice of medical career. Caesalpinus (1524–1603) publishes *Questiones Medicae*, incidentally discussing pulmonary and systemic circulation.

1597. Receives Bachelor's degree from Cambridge. Expedition of Earl of Essex and Sir Walter Raleigh against the Spaniards.

1598. Began medical studies at Padua (in the elite *Universitas juristarum*), scene of the triumphs of Vesalius (1514–1564), R. Columbus (1516–1559), Fallopius (1523–1562), and now of H. Fabricius of Aquapendente (1537–1619), Casserius (1561–1616), Galilei (1564–1642), and Sanctorius (1561–1636). Having just erected a new anatomical theater, Fabricius was loved and respected for his charity, skill, and learning. Harvey apparently became one of his favorite pupils, and even *helped in experiments* (*De generatione*, 6th exercise).

1600. Elected *conciliarius* of "English nation" at Padua. Fabricius publishes his *De formato fœtu*. Giordano Bruno burned at Rome. Founding of East India Company. Gilbert's *De magnete*.

1601. Re-elected *conciliarius.* Treason and execution of Earl of Essex.

1602. Awarded diploma (April 25) of Doctor of Physic at Padua, with special notations regarding his skill. Returned to England and received doctorate in medicine from Cambridge. Shakespeare's *Hamlet.*

1603. Publication of Fabricius' *De venarum ostiolis.* Death of Queen Elizabeth, accession of James I.

1604. Admitted a Candidate of the Royal College of Physicians (October 5). Married (November 24) Elizabeth Browne (1580–1645?), daughter of Dr. Lancelot Browne, physician to James I. Lived at St. Martin's, Ludgate. Plague in London.

1605. Death of Mother (November 18) at Folkestone, in her fiftieth year. Death of Father-in-law. Harvey seems to have been well fixed financially. His brothers were wealthy merchants, trading in the Levant. Gun Powder Conspiracy.

1607. Elected Fellow of the Royal College of Physicians (June 5). Settlement of Jamestown, Virginia.

1609. With King's support, sued for the reversion of Physician to St. Bartholomew's Hospital (February 25). Charged as Physician to "Old Bart's" (October 14). Hendrick Hudson anchors the Half-Moon in Hudson River.

1611. King James' Authorized Version of the English Bible.

1613. Elected Censor of the Royal College of Physicians. High cost of living; increasing friction between King and Parliament; religious squabbles. Rise of Puritanism.

1615. Appointed (August 4) Lumleian lecturer, Royal College of Physicians. Detailed duties and salary equivalent to Regius Professorship of Physic at Oxford

or Cambridge (see D'Arcy Power's biography, London, 1897, p. 39).

1616. Delivered (April) first "visceral lecture" at Royal College of Physicians, in manuscript notes in which is his first account of the circulation of the blood. Death of Shakespeare and Cervantes.

1618. Appointed (February 3) Physician Extraordinary to James I, and promised post of Physician in Ordinary as soon as it became vacant. The Lord Chancellor, Francis Bacon, his patient, but no sympathy between them. Start of Thirty Years' War. *Pharmacopoeia Londinensis.*

1620. Publication of Bacon's *Novum Organum.* Puritans settle in New England.

1625. Death of King James I, accession of Charles I.

1627. Appointed (December 3) Elect of Royal College of Physicians, one of eight "directors."

1628. Publication of *Exercitatio anatomica de motu cordis et sanguinis in animalibus,* at Frankfort. Elected Treasurer of Royal College of Physicians. Birth of Marcello Malpighi (March 10). Parliament's *Petition of Right.*

1630. Journeys through France and Spain with James Stuart, Duke of Lennox, at King's order. Plagues, wars, and famines. King struggling with Parliament. Appointed Physician in Ordinary to Charles I. Jacob Primrose, licensed to practice with Harvey's consent, publishes first attack on his doctrine of the circulation.

1632. Petitions King to restrict sale of poisons.

1633. Travels with Charles and Court to Scotland. Tactless aggravation of religious animosities. Drew up rules governing St. Bartholomew's Hospital, in which he subordinates surgeons to physicians. Reflection of oppressive court tactics? Recantation of Galilei.

1634. Lancashire witches. Harvey examined and exonerated several suspects.

1635. Accused (November 17) of malpractice by Barber-Surgeons. Revenge? Autopsy report (November 16) on Thomas Parr, reputed to have lived 152 years. Richelieu founded Academie Francaise.

1636. Accompanied Lord Arundel on diplomatic mission to Vienna. Tried to convince Caspar Hoffman at Nuremberg of truth of circulation. Visited Italy. Harvard College founded.

1637. Religious riots in Scotland. Covenanters.

1639. Went with Charles and Lord Arundel against the Scotch.

1640. Sued heirs of Lord Lumley to recover salary. Meeting of Long Parliament. "Grand Remonstrance" against Charles.

1641. Trial and execution of Strafford.

1642. Charles and Court fled London (August) Civil War. Harvey's quarters looted, and valuable papers lost. Death of Galilei. Birth of Newton. Harvey in charge of the Princes (Charles II and James II) at Battle of Edgehill (October), and tends wounded. Browne's *Religio Medici*. Made Doctor of Physic at Oxford (December 7).

1643. Retired from service at St. Bartholomew's. Death of Brothers Matthew and Michael. Taught Charles Scarborough, his successor. Accession of Louis XIV.

1645. Elected Warden of Merton College, Oxford. Did he influence Willis, Highmore, Lower, or Wren? Death of Brother John. Death of wife?

1646. Fled from Oxford with King (April 27). Returned to London.

1648. Retired to live with Brothers Eliab and Daniel. Afflicted with gout. The younger Riolan publishes critique of Harvey's doctrine of the circulation. War of the Fronde. Peace of Westphalia, ending terrible Thirty Years' War, and acknowledging independence of the Netherlands. Sydenham (1624–1689) made bachelor of medicine at Oxford.

1649. Harvey from Cambridge writes two letters to Riolan answering the attack on his demonstration. Execution of Charles I. Cromwell subdues Great Britain and Ireland.

1650. Visited at Christmas time by his friend Dr. George Ent, who obtained manuscript of essay on generation.

1651. Publication of *Exercitationes de generatione animalium.* Offered anonymously to build library for Royal College of Physicians. Pecquet publishes account of thoracic duct. Harvey writes to Dr. Paul M. Slegel, of Hamburg, thanking him for defending his work against Riolan. Meets John Aubrey, his first biographer.

1652. Letter to Dr. R. Morison of Paris criticizing Pecquet's conclusions. Royal College of Physicians placed bust of Harvey in new library.

1653. First English edition of the *De motu cordis.* Parliament disbanded.

1654. Refuses to accept Presidency of Royal College of Physicians.

1657. Died on June 3. Buried in Hempstead Church.

THE BODY OF WILLIAM HARVEY "LAPT IN LEAD"
Deposited in a marble sarcophagus
in the Hempstead Church
by the Royal College of Physicians of London
St. Luke's Day, 1883.

INDEX

Index